Zap 07

'What made you offer to help me?'

Taken aback, Carla stared at Daniel blankly. 'I'm not sure what you mean . . .'

'I mean you virtually saved my life,' he persisted quietly, his expression obscure. 'That would have been enough. Why did you offer to let me stay here?'

'That's a silly question,' she protested, shaking her head. 'You needed somewhere to recover. You had no obvious place to go. . . it seemed the only thing I could do!'

D1635753

Dear Reader

Summer might be drawing to an end—but don't despair! This month's selection of exciting love stories is guaranteed to bring back a little sunshine! Why not let yourself be transported to the beauty of a Caribbean paradise—or perhaps you'd prefer the exotic mystery of Egypt? All in the company of a charming and devastatingly handsome hero, naturally! Of course, you don't have to go abroad to find true romance—and when you're a Mills & Boon reader you don't even need to step outside your front door! Just relax with this book, and you'll see what we mean...

The Editor

Having abandoned her first intended career for marriage, **Rosalie Ash** spent several years as a bilingual personal assistant to the managing director of a leisure group. She now lives in Warwickshire with her husband, and daughters Kate and Abby, and her lifelong enjoyment of writing has led to her career as a novelist. Her interests include languages, travel and research for her books, reading, and visits to the Royal Shakespeare Theatre in nearby Stratford-upon-Avon. Other pleasures include swimming, yoga and country walks.

Recent titles by the same author:

ORIGINAL SIN
AN IMPORTED WIFE
APOLLO'S LEGEND

MYTHS OF
THE MOON

BY
ROSALIE ASH

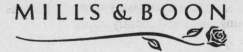

MILLS & BOON

MILLS & BOON LIMITED
ETON HOUSE, 18-24 PARADISE ROAD
RICHMOND, SURREY TW9 1SR

DID YOU PURCHASE THIS BOOK WITHOUT A COVER?

If you did, you should be aware it is **stolen property** as it was reported *unsold and destroyed* by a retailer. Neither the Author nor the publisher has received any payment for this book.

All the characters in this book have no existence outside the imagination of the Author, and have no relation whatsoever to anyone bearing the same name or names. They are not even distantly inspired by any individual known or unknown to the Author, and all the incidents are pure invention.

All Rights Reserved. The text of this publication or any part thereof may not be reproduced or transmitted in any form or by any means, electronic or mechanical, including photocopying, recording, storage in an information retrieval system, or otherwise, without the written permission of the publisher.

This book is sold subject to the condition that it shall not, by way of trade or otherwise, be lent, resold, hired out or otherwise circulated without the prior consent of the publisher in any form of binding or cover other than that in which it is published and without a similar condition including this condition being imposed on the subsequent purchaser.

MILLS & BOON and the Rose Device are trademarks of the publisher.

First published in Great Britain 1994 by Mills & Boon Limited

© Rosalie Ash 1994

Australian copyright 1994   Philippine copyright 1994 This edition 1994

ISBN 0 263 78618 8

Set in Times Roman 11 on 12 pt. 01-9409-45052 C

Made and printed in Great Britain

CHAPTER ONE

HE'D fallen asleep. But, in spite of that long, hard body sprawled in the red wing-chair by the fire, he managed to retain an air of wary vigilance. In a position when most men would look vulnerable, this one looked threatening...

Carla hesitated in the doorway, tray in hand. Then she crept quietly into the cottage, and closed the front door behind her. She could feel her heart beating a touch faster than normal. Carefully, soundlessly, she put the tray down on the black oak sideboard by the door, and stared at him.

Who *was* he?

Not for the first time in the past twenty-four hours, she wondered bleakly what on earth she'd got herself into. It was all very well being a good Samaritan. And she being naturally stubborn, the words of warning from friends in the village had merely made her more determined to offer help...

She had the accommodation. She'd had this small self-contained cottage converted last year, from the stables of her stone farmhouse. She rented it out to holidaymakers in the summer. It had a superb view over the bay, and down along a mystical, timeless stretch of south Cornish coastline. It even overlooked the precise spot where the cliff accident had sent ripples of concern through this tiny Cornish village. The cottage was tailor-made for the accident victim's recovery...

It wasn't as if she was sharing her own *house* with a total stranger, was it? Back in the safety of the farm, she could shoot the bolts and turn the heavy old keys in the locks, and barricade herself in against potential night-time assaults, should he prove to be the crazed rapist of the village post-mistress's imagination...

And it wasn't as if she was a naïve, impressionable young girl, her reasoning ran on, bolstering her nerve. She was a twenty-five-year-old widow, a successful writer of detective novels, nobody's fool...

So...why was she standing here, throat dry as sandpaper, staring at her mysterious lodger as if he were Jack the Ripper?

Catching sight of her wind-blown appearance in the big oval mirror above the fireplace, she pushed her fingers hastily through her tousled brown bob. She made a rueful face. Rufus had always complained that she didn't take enough trouble with her appearance. And since his death in an accident last year she'd probably taken even less. Bundled up in heavy Aran polo neck, green cord jeans, and ancient, battered Barbour jacket, she felt quite sure that Rufus would have disapproved. But then she and Rufus should never have got married. They'd discovered that, very shortly after their wedding. Her late husband had envisaged a wife as someone who spent mornings at the hairdresser, afternoons painting her nails, and evenings cooking cordon bleu meals before slipping into slinky lace nightwear for torrid nights of pleasure. He had disapproved of just about everything he'd discovered about Carla, during their three brief years of marriage, and wasted no time in seeking consolation elsewhere...

Carla chewed her lip indecisively, wavering over whether to retreat, with the meal-tray, and return later. Lurking under the silver foil was a robust beef and red wine casserole, judged by her to be ideal food to fortify a large six-foot male recovering from concussion and temporary amnesia.

Could it endure a re-heat in the microwave, and still retain recuperative properties? she wondered wryly...

'Hello.'

The husky voice made her jump with nervous reaction. The black-fringed eyes were open. Her visitor was looking at her, with a bemused expression.

'Oh, you're awake...! Sorry, did *I* wake you?'

'Possibly.' His mouth twisted in wry humour. 'But don't feel guilty. Something's smelling good on that tray. Would it be presumptuous to hope it's for me?'

She smiled stiffly.

'Yes. It's beef and red wine... with mushrooms. I hope you like mushrooms?'

'Sounds delicious.'

He made a visible effort to straighten up, and lever himself to standing. With his left arm still in a sling, his progress was hindered. But he made it. In the low-ceilinged cottage, Carla found his height less alarming than she'd expected. Tall, lean, black-haired, with that villainous growth of stubble on his jaw, he should surely have exuded even more threat. But, with the slight hint of unsteadiness in his stance, perversely enough he now looked more vulnerable than when he'd been asleep.

With a rush of remorse, she grabbed the tray from the sideboard and hurried over to him.

'Please, don't stand up! Oh, dear, now I feel even worse. You're supposed to be resting, getting better! I'm afraid I make a lousy nurse...'

'I don't need a nurse,' he pointed out shortly, subsiding into the chair again with a grimace. 'Physically the hospital pronounced me dischargeable. All I need is a good night's sleep away from the chaos of a public ward, and my mind back.'

'You haven't lost your mind,' she pointed out, quietly. She thrust the tray on to muscular, denim-clad knees, and lifted the foil to reveal a hearty portion of the casserole, flanked by creamed potatoes and buttered cabbage. 'Just your memory. And it will come back soon. The less you worry about getting it back, the quicker it will come. That's what the doctors said. And staying here, where you had the accident, should hurry up your recovery...'

She was wittering nervously, she realised, annoyed with herself. She stopped for a moment, meeting the contained expression in his face. Somewhere deep inside, she felt an unwelcome lurch of awareness.

Beneath the mass of straight black hair, his face was firm-jawed, with a powerfully aquiline nose. Even with the distraction of the pad of lint stuck to one temple, and the bluish bruising on one high cheekbone, it was a daunting sort of face. Maybe it was his eyes. He had lynx-like, penetrating eyes. Eyes which made her feel as if her private thoughts might be analysed, maybe before she'd analysed them herself. They were deep-set, beneath straight dark eyebrows. Against very clear whites, the irises were a curious shade of green. Not emerald, not sage. More the colour of the rock-pools on the beach on a cloudy day.

She straightened up abruptly, and stepped back. 'I hope you like cabbage?' she finished up foolishly. She felt unsettled by the faint flicker of humour in his gaze. 'But leave it if you don't. I . . . I made sure everything can be easily eaten with just a fork. Can you remember what you like and what you don't like to eat?'

'Cabbage is just fine.'

There was a pause, slightly awkward. He smiled a touch more widely, revealing even white teeth. Then he began eating, sublimely unselfconscious of her watching eyes.

'Well, I'll leave you to it . . .'

She retreated to the door, then hesitated.

'Unless...' She sought for the right words, desperate not to appear pushy, or, heaven forbid, forward in any way. She'd no wish to give him the wrong impression. 'Unless you'd like some company?'

There was a silence. Then he nodded, with a brief, slightly haggard smile.

'Thanks. I could do with some company.'

'I'll go and get my dinner, and join you,' she said calmly, darting across the wind-swept cobbled yard and returning with her own meal on a tray, with a bottle of red wine and two glasses. She put the tray on the low black oak coffee-table in front of the fire, discarded her Barbour on the hook by the door, and began to uncork the wine.

'It must feel so strange,' she added, busying herself determinedly to maintain her poise under his scrutiny, 'not being able to remember who you are, or what you were doing here...'

The dark head nodded slowly.

'Like waking up in a dark cellar, and not being able to find the light switch.' The thoughtful words were tinged with irony.

Carla glanced at him quickly, handing over a glass of red wine.

'When you're feeling like it, perhaps a walk along the same cliff-path might trigger something?'

'Isn't the path barred to walkers now?'

'Well, yes. But you can still get partway, along the upper path. Close enough to see where the ground gave way...'

Involuntarily, she shuddered in memory. The recent drama rushed back to haunt her. Dusk falling, a stiff breeze blowing off the ocean, and with no warning near-death had beckoned, right in front of her eyes...

She'd taken a break from her intense concentration on her word-processor screen, leaning back to stretch and rub her eyes, and contemplate the next intricate twist of her plot. She'd been so absorbed in writing, she hadn't noticed how dark it was getting. The greenish glow from her VDU was the only light in her study, and she'd been about to reach across and click on the Anglepoise lamp when her attention was caught by a movement on the cliff-top. From her study window the rugged sweep of coastline had been framed with perfect clarity. The sky was that brilliant, unreal shade of pale, duck-egg blue that came when the sun set on a winter evening. A full moon had already been visible. The movement she'd seen had been a man, walking along the coastal path. One moment the tall, broad-shouldered figure had been striding along in the direction of the farm. The next moment, with a muffled, doom-laden rumble of falling rock and crumbling earth, he'd disappeared over the edge of the cliff. A cloud of dust had risen to blot out her view. When it had subsided, all that remained was a jagged hole in the side of the cliff.

Seized with horror, she'd sprung up instinctively, hand over her mouth. Then, so stunned by the suddenness of the scene, she'd felt frozen to the spot. Common sense had finally reasserted itself. Snatching up the telephone, she'd rung the emergency services. Then she'd found a torch, dashed from the house, grabbed a coil of rope from the now empty barn, and rushed down the lane and out on to the cliff-top, to see if she could help. Inching as close as she dared, her heart pounding and her throat dry with fear, she'd steeled herself to peer over the edge. Dreading seeing a broken, bloodied body down below, she'd felt a slight surge of relief. The man had looked to be unconscious, but at least he was in one piece. Or as far as she could see, anyway, in the rapidly fading light... And he hadn't plummeted all the way down to the rocky beach below. The fall of earth had somehow blocked his fall. The pile of rocks and earth had rolled halfway down the cliff, then come to a halt against the resistance of gorse bushes and brambles clinging to the cliff-side. The man's face had been deathly white, though. And an ugly gash on his temple had been trickling ominously red.

Heart squeezed in her chest, trembling with apprehension, she'd called down to him, without response. All she'd been able to do was sit there, while the sky grew darker and the moon grew brighter, watching fearfully in case of further subsidence, until the coastguard, and the rescue helicopter from Culdrose, had arrived...

'Are you all right?'

Her visitor was regarding her with bleak amusement.

'I thought you were dead, you know,' she said ruefully, pouring some wine into her own glass and taking a fortifying sip. 'You looked like a ghost, lying down there on the cliff.'

'Sorry. But, as you can see, I'm very much alive. In body, if not in mind.' He took a drink of the red wine, and made a wry face. 'I doubt if alcohol is the approved cure for extradural haemorrhage and amnesia, somehow.'

'Oh . . . sorry.'

'Stop apologising.' The sea-green eyes levelled calmly on her face. 'If anyone here should be constantly apologising, Miss Julyan, it's me. I'm imposing on your time and hospitality. Being waited on, fussed over. And frankly, you're a brave woman. You don't know who I am. I could be a psychiatric case, a dangerous criminal.'

She bit her lip. Her earlier doubts were still so fresh in her mind, she stopped herself just in time from blushing bright red.

'You don't strike me as either.'

He shrugged slightly. There was a gleam of frustrated humour in his eyes.

'I don't feel like either. The hellish thing is not knowing.'

They stared at each other in silence for a few moments.

'It's going to take some detective work, that's all,' she said at last. 'It's a question of piecing together all the small things you *can* remember, until something jolts the rest...'

'All I know is that my name's Daniel.'

'True... if that note was addressed to you.'

He frowned, then made a face.

'It was in my shirt pocket. "Daniel, darling, hope you've everything you need—see you soon, all my love, R.",' he quoted flatly. 'Are you saying I could have been about to give the note to someone? That I could be "R"?'

'Well...' The flaw in this theory had just struck her. She was too used to thinking up strange twists in her detective books. She coloured a little as he laughed.

'If so, it could be that "Daniel, darling" and I have a relationship I don't feel ready to admit to!' He grinned. He was watching her embarrassment with a merciless gleam.

'Well, there's something else you know about yourself.' She covered her loss of poise with a stab of teasing humour. 'You're heterosexual!'

'As far as I can tell from analysing my thought-processes,' he agreed.

There was an ironic gleam in his slow appraisal of Carla's flushed, heart-shaped face, her slender figure hidden by the Aran sweater. The unabashed curiosity made her stiffen slightly. Then the implication of his words sank in. The heat which abruptly engulfed her was so all-consuming, she felt as if invisible flames were licking around her. The lurch of awareness was back, double strength. She was horrified to feel a shiver of physical reaction, new and deeply unnerving.

She looked quickly away, praying that he hadn't noticed her hot cheeks and erratic pulse-rate...

'Don't look so anxious, Miss Julyan.' He grinned. 'I'm in no state to put any theories to the test. Besides, you brought sex into the conversation, not me!'

'I wasn't intending to look anxious.' She defended herself as calmly as she felt able. There was an annoying huskiness in her voice. 'And please stop calling me Miss Julyan...'

'What would you prefer to be called? Ma'am?'

'Carla. I'd prefer to be called Carla.' She hung on to her temper with difficulty.

'Then we'll seal the intimacy. You call me Daniel,' he said irrepressibly, finishing his meal with a nod of approval. 'And you're a great cook, Carla. One of these days you'll make a husband a very happy man.'

'My husband is dead.' She said it without inflexion, embarrassed by his lack of knowledge. 'He was thrown from his horse in a riding accident, a year ago. And, to be quite truthful, he wasn't a very happy man when he was alive...'

What had prompted her to say such a thing? The confession seemed to hang in the air between them, out of place and unwarranted.

Daniel leaned back in the wing-chair, watching her intently. To cover her confusion, she stood up and took the tray from his knees, carried it to the sideboard. Pausing there, she pressed her hands to her hot cheeks for a few seconds, and drew a deep breath before she came back to sit down opposite him again.

'You reverted to your maiden name?' His curiosity was clearly aroused.

'I . . . yes.'

He was searching her face, a dissecting light in his eyes.

'Do I detect that your marriage was an unhappy one, Carla?' There was a gentler note in his voice.

'What makes you say that?' She knew she sounded idiotic. She'd virtually told him it was unhappy, hadn't she?

'Dropped your married name only a year after being widowed? And what you said just now? About your husband?' he suggested, quietly ironic.

'Sorry—ignore what I said, would you?' She managed to smile at him, sipping some wine while she grappled with her composure. 'Rufus died just over a year ago. I guess I'm . . . I'm not really over it all yet . . .'

'I'd say it takes a lot longer than a year to mourn the loss of someone you love.' Daniel's face was shadowed. The flicker of the fire lit one side only.

To evade further discussion, she nodded quickly.

'That's assuming, of course, that you did love your husband?'

'I...' She stopped, staring at him, mauve-blue eyes wide with indignation. 'What a *strange* question!' she finished up coldly. 'I appreciate you've got time on your hands, but if you're going to spend it making rude speculations about me I might regret offering to have you here...!'

There was a brief silence.

'Would you like me to leave?'

'No, of course not!' she amended irritably, cross with herself for losing her cool.

'Thanks.' The edge in the deep voice was difficult to fathom. There was certainly more to it than gratitude, or remorse.

She forced a laugh. 'I offered you company this evening. All we seem to have done is bicker!'

'We don't seem destined to hit it off,' he confirmed evenly.

For some reason, this analysis made her feel even angrier.

'The trouble is, we seem to have got round to talking about *me*, when the idea is to talk about you,' she said hurriedly. 'I'm convinced that if we adopt a logical approach to your memory-loss, something will trigger its return.'

'You mean, like tracking back over your movements when you lose your wallet?'

'Something like that. Why not?'

'Why not indeed?' His smile was far from reassuring. 'You're not a policewoman, by any chance?'

'No. I write detective stories...'

His eyebrows lifted. 'Are you published?'

'Yes. I write under the pseudonym of Carl Julyan.'

He looked unflatteringly blank for a few moments, then his eyes betrayed a flicker of recognition.

'Carl Julyan? *You're* Carl Julyan? Creator of Inspector Jack Tresawna?'

'Yes. Have you read any of my books?'

'I must have done.'

'And did you enjoy them?' she felt forced to enquire, goaded by his lack of comment.

'I did. Sorry, I wasn't intending any insult,' he added evenly; 'I was waiting to see if this revelation brought anything else filtering back to mind.'

'Has it?'

He shook his head slowly.

'I don't think so.'

'But you can remember reading Carl Julyan books. That's a breakthrough, of a kind!' she said, excitement making her eyes glow. 'Maybe if you reread one or two your memory might be jolted by something?'

'Possibly. Although I'd hazard a guess that fiction is unlikely to.' Lifting his uninjured hand to his forehead, he massaged his temples with a sudden, jerky motion.

'Are you all right?' She found herself quelling an instinctive urge to jump up and fuss like a mother hen.

'Yes...I'm all right.' He dropped his hand quickly.

'Have you got a headache?'

He smiled bleakly. 'Since I woke up in a hospital bed three weeks ago, I can't remember *not* having a headache. I gather from the doctors that headaches and head injuries tend to go together.'

The put-down seemed deliberate.

'I'm sorry, I'm probably tiring you out with all this talking. Would you like anything else to eat? Or coffee?'

'No, thank you. Nothing else.'

'Not even home-made apple pie and clotted cream?' she tempted lightly.

'Another time, perhaps.'

Carla stood up decisively. 'Let me get you a painkiller, then I'll leave you to go to bed...'

'I've got pain-killers. I can manage to open the bottle and swallow a couple all by myself.'

Again, the sarcasm was unprovoked. She was evidently getting badly on his nerves. Wincing inwardly, she turned away.

'Wait...' Was there the faintest tinge of vulnerability in his curt voice? 'Tell me something, before you go...'

She turned back to look at him. There was the shadow of physical pain in his eyes. In spite of her annoyance, a wave of sympathy and helplessness washed over her. This man was suffering, physically and mentally. And one thing was certain—he wasn't a natural patient. He loathed being ill, loathed being at a disadvantage, hated being virtually dependent on others for his recovery. And she could think of few worse mental tortures than being unable to remember who you were...

The insight made his prickly behaviour more understandable. She felt faintly guilty for allowing his defensive taunting to provoke her. She definitely hadn't missed her vocation in nursing, she reflected ruefully.

'Yes?'

'What made you offer to help me?'

Taken aback, she stared at him blankly. 'I'm not sure what you mean...'

'I mean you virtually saved my life,' he persisted quietly, his expression obscure. 'That would have been enough. Why did you offer to let me stay here?'

'I didn't save your life...!' She met the penetrating stare with a fresh warmth in her cheeks. 'I just happened to be looking out of my study window at the right moment, that's all...'

'Same thing. If you hadn't been, I'd probably have lain halfway down the cliff all night. If I hadn't been found promptly, the chances of surgery succeeding would have been diminished. I have it on reliable medical authority. So I was already in your debt, Carla. Why all this as well?'

She gazed at him in mounting confusion.

'That's a silly question,' she protested, shaking her head. 'It's obvious why. You needed somewhere to recover. You had no obvious place to go.

No access to money or anything...it seemed the only thing I could do!'

'Not necessarily. The police, the hospital, Social Services, any of them could have offered a solution. So why you?'

The narrowed gaze searched her flushed face.

'Well, I suppose having seen the accident, having found you...' she caught her breath, feeling herself getting angry again and this time not at all sure why '...I felt a kind of responsibility to help. And staying so close to where you were walking...I thought it could bring your memory back quicker...'

What was he getting at? Did he suspect her of some ulterior motive? Was he implying that she must be the typical 'lonely widow'? Or, worse still, the typical 'merry widow'? Her heart seemed to contract in her chest. What was it about this man which seemed doomed to rub her up the wrong way? Did there have to be some hidden motive for offering simple kindness?

'I think you should get an early night,' she advised, adopting her most formal manner. 'Can you manage by yourself...?'

'You're not offering a full nursing service, by any chance?' he teased lightly. 'Because I think I can still remember how to wash my face and clean my teeth.'

'Good.' Hateful, sardonic, ungrateful man. Why was she wasting any sympathy on him at all? 'In that case, I'll say goodnight.'

'Good night, Carla.'

She risked one parting glance at him, and wished she hadn't. The cool green eyes seemed to be far too dissecting, as he observed her suppressed resentment.

Loading everything on to one tray, she made a bolt for the relative safety of the main house, and her own kitchen.

She felt as if she'd just been put through some psychological mangle. Daniel Whoever-he-was was the most *disruptive* man she'd ever met.

With angry precision she unloaded and reloaded the dishwasher, stacked fluted white porcelain in dark oak cupboards, wiped green-tiled worktops, then finally collapsed on to the ancient oak settle by the Aga. She glared distractedly at Moppy, a fluffy, apricot Persian, stretched as close to the warmth as he could get. Moppy stared back, and blinked lazily, golden eyes forgiving. With an apologetic smile she reached down to stroke him. He might be hopeless as a country mousing cat, but he was a comforting presence, and she loved him dearly...

She thought about phoning someone, anything to calm this strange agitation inside her. But it was gone ten, too late to ring her friend Becky at Carperrow Farm—she'd have tucked her small, well-behaved daughter into her cot and leapt eagerly into bed with her husband Tom by now. And ringing her mother, probably still engrossed in a bridge four in her genteel Regency flat in Bath, was equally out of the question. She'd immediately think some dreadful disaster had occurred.

Carla shook herself out of her reverie and stood up. She could ring Becky in the morning, console herself with a light-hearted natter with a friend, before buckling down to work on chapter fifteen. She had a deadline on this book. Getting sidetracked and thrown off-centre by Daniel's overpowering personality was the very last thing she needed...

But upstairs in bed, showered, hair vigorously brushed, teeth energetically scrubbed, clad in demure pale blue silk pyjamas, she lay wide awake and tense beneath her cream duvet.

It was his parting probe which had unnerved her. He wasn't a mind-reader. That was too far-fetched. But even so... his questions had made her examine a disturbing truth. In some way, some unexplained way, she'd been aware of an underlying emotion behind her practical offers of help...

Frowning into the darkness, she tried to make sense of it. She couldn't. All she knew was, ever since that moonlit night, when she'd kept her lonely vigil on the cliff-top, she'd felt this invisible pull...

It was scary, she decided angrily. And it was ridiculous. Was she behaving like Inspector Tresawna's rather fey female sidekick, in her novels? Imagining psychic auras?

The best thing she could do, she decided, squeezing her eyes shut and willing herself to sleep, was help her mysterious visitor to get his memory back, and get him out of her life, in that order, as fast as she could.

But, even though he was across the yard, in the cottage, she was *aware* of Daniel's presence. Mentally, and, to her continuing shame, physically. A feathering of goose-bumps broke out all over her skin, simply at the memory of those cool green eyes ... The sensation was so strong, he could be standing here, in the same room ...

With a burst of anger, she sat up and clicked on her light, glaring round the bedroom to allay her ridiculous imaginings. Then she subsided back against the pillows, and tossed feverishly on to her side.

CHAPTER TWO

'YOU'RE taking a risk,' Becky said, across the table.

As if by telepathy, her friend had appeared this morning, bearing a basket of eggs and a big bunch of late chrysanthemums and Michaelmas daisies from her sheltered, south-facing walled garden.

'Don't you start...!'

'It's true. Tom and I are worried about you.'

'It's only for a maximum of three weeks,' Carla pointed out. 'I've got some visitors booked in for a pre-Christmas break then...'

'Still, I thought I'd pop in and offer moral support,' Becky said stubbornly.

'Thanks. I must confess, I feel in need of it.' Carla made a wry face as she glanced over her shoulder, busily putting the glorious flowers in water. Their sharp, spicy fragrance filled the air. 'These are wonderful, Becky. Especially so late in November. My favourite flowers, and my favourite colours.' She thrust the last sprig of mauve daisies between autumn-gold and russet, and stood back to admire her handiwork.

'Clever you. My flower arrangements always look...basic.' Becky laughed, sipping her coffee. 'Why Rufus never cherished your talents I'll never know!'

There was an awkward pause, and Becky groaned to herself.

'Sorry—my big mouth...'

'No, it's OK.' Carla turned quickly, and came to sit down, her eyes clouded. 'Just because Rufus is dead it doesn't make it taboo to mention his name, you know!'

'No, I know...'

'And do you know something?' Carla rested her chin on her hand, and met her friend's eyes thoughtfully. 'I don't feel bitter about him any more. It occurred to me recently that poor old Rufus got a raw deal when he married me. I was so engrossed in trying to establish my writing career, I never had time for fancy flower arrangements or elaborate meals—it was a minor miracle if I ran a duster over the furniture or made it to the supermarket! It's only since he died that I've become better at domesticity! Ironic, isn't it? Looking back, maybe it's hard to blame him for being unfaithful...'

'Carla, that's the most ridiculous thing I ever heard...!'

'Well, I'm not sure... I wasn't what he thought he was getting. I expect he felt duped...'

'I know it's wrong to speak ill of the dead,' Becky said flatly, 'but Rufus didn't want a wife and equal partner, he wanted a subservient little slave to indulge his every selfish whim. Frankly, Carla, Rufus was a waste of space, and you know it...'

'Becky...!'

'He spent most of his time subtly ridiculing you, to compensate for his own weak character! Undermining your confidence in your writing, your appearance, everything...while he wallowed in misery about the unfairness of his life, his failures in business, the injustice of that partnership that went sour, started drowning his bitterness in whisky...I mean, I'm sorry about his tragic accident, Carla, but the man ruined your self-confidence!'

'Becky...'

'The trouble with you,' Becky drove home her point, 'is that you've never had enough self-esteem! You've got this image of yourself as hopeless and inept—you've never shaken that off since your dad used to tell you how disappointed he was in you! Now here you are, a big success as a detective-writer, and you put yourself down still; you lock yourself away like a recluse...'

Carla laughed ruefully. 'Have you quite finished? I do not lock myself away like a recluse. I enjoy my own company...'

'But you don't make any effort to socialise, Carla.' Becky thrust an impatient hand through her short blonde hair, and sighed at the stubborn tilt to her friend's chin. 'I honestly think that husband of yours has put you off men for life,' Becky added crisply.

Carla gazed back, her pale, heart-shaped face set determinedly within its frame of straight dark hair, steady resistance in the large, purplish-blue eyes.

'Maybe he did.' She shrugged carelessly. 'I just wasn't any good at being the meek, biddable wife. To top the lot, I wasn't even any good in bed...'

Carla's grin lightened the words, but behind her eyes was a pain she kept fiercely dampened down.

'Huh!' Becky's snort was derisive. 'You and your guilt complex! It never occurred to you that it could have been the other way round...?'

'Oh, Becky...!'

A knock on the half-open stable-door to the kitchen made Carla swivel round abruptly. Daniel stood there, a quizzical look on his face.

'Good morning. Sorry to interrupt,' he said evenly, nodding and smiling briefly at Becky before glancing back to Carla. 'Do you have some milk and eggs I could use?'

Carla caught a fleeting glimpse of Becky's widened brown eyes as she took her first proper look at the stranger the whole village was gossiping about. Then she resolutely avoided her friend's gaze.

'Of course—but I was going to bring you some breakfast,' she said hastily, standing up and darting to the fridge. 'I've got bacon and tomatoes grilling at the moment...'

She felt hot all over. How long had he been standing there, listening? How much of her conversation with Becky had he overheard? Why did he have to creep up on her like that?

'Maybe it was the delicious smell that lured me over.' He grinned, raking a hand through his dark hair, and eyeing her flushed face. 'But it's all right, I can easily cook for myself. The problem is obtaining the ingredients!'

His rueful tone reminded her forcibly how dependent he was for support.

'Whatever you'd rather do,' she agreed. 'But, since I'm already cooking for you this morning, maybe you'd like to join me here? This is my friend Becky Pascoe, from Carperrow Farm. Becky, this is . . . Daniel.'

'Delighted to meet you.' Daniel reached to shake Becky's outstretched hand, his expression unreadable. Carla found the slight pinkness in her friend's cheeks oddly reassuring. It wasn't just her, then. Other females, even down-to-earth and happily married ones like Becky, were affected by this man's subtle charisma . . .

With enviable composure, he sat down at the table. He was wearing a checked shirt, denim jeans, and a ribbed crew-neck jumper in dark forest-green which emphasised the colour of his cyes, not to mention the impressively lean width of his chest and shoulders. He'd discarded the sling the hospital had discharged him with yesterday. His left wrist was bandaged, but he seemed to be flexing the fingers deliberately, as though impatient for recovery.

'How are you getting on?' Becky was asking. 'Do you have any idea yet why you came to Penuthna?'

'I haven't a clue.' His expression was wry. 'But the fact that no one seems to have missed me points to a holiday, maybe.'

'True. But the police haven't been able to trace where you could have been staying, have they?'

'Not yet.' He flexed his shoulders, as if easing hidden tension. Carla busied herself dishing up bacon, tomatoes and sausages, while Becky chatted vivaciously, an excited glitter in her eyes. Daniel's replies were brief and humorous. As Carla brought the plates to the table, Becky jumped up and excused herself reluctantly.

'That looks wonderful! I'd love to stay and eat with you, but Tom's minding the baby so I'd better dash back. Come up and see us soon...' She smiled from Carla to Daniel, adding quickly, 'In fact, come and have dinner. Both of you. I'll ring you, Carla...'

When her friend had gone, Carla met Daniel's shuttered gaze with an inward groan of embarrassment. How could Becky be so... insensitive? Practically pairing them off together! It was ridiculous. One minute voicing concern for her safety with a stranger in the house, the next inviting them to dinner as if they were a long-established *couple*!

'Sorry about that,' she said lightly. 'I don't think Becky knows quite how to treat you...'

'How do you think I should be treated?' he queried calmly. 'Like a circus freak or like a normal human being?'

'There's no need to be so... touchy,' she felt compelled to retort. 'I didn't mean that... I mean, I just don't want anyone getting the wrong idea.'

'And what idea would that be?' He sounded amused.

'Oh, for heaven's sake, do I have to spell it out?'

'I'm afraid you do.' There was a silky trace of mockery beneath the light tone.

Furious, she sat down, watched him begin to eat and forced herself to do likewise. 'This is a very small village. Gossip is one of the few pastimes available to people...'

'It's bound to happen,' he pointed out easily. 'A woman on her own offers accommodation to a strange man—tongues wag. You should have thought of that before you issued your invitation.'

She froze in the act of slicing her grilled tomato, large mauve-blue eyes simmering with annoyance.

'You know, I could almost get the idea that you're *enjoying* this!'

He shrugged slightly. 'Having a blank slate for a memory is no joke. But watching you tiptoeing around your own conscience, juggling with your guilt complexes, is reasonably entertaining.'

'Oh, *is* it?'

'Perhaps the word "entertaining" is too offensive, Carla. Sorry. Maybe "intriguing" is a better word.' He didn't sound particularly sorry. The sea-green gaze was amused, and irritatingly aloof. Carla pushed her plate away, and regarded him balefully. What kind of viper had she opened her doors to?

'Tea or coffee? And what *guilt* complexes would these be?' she enquired at last, adopting her sweetest tone.

'Coffee, please. Black, no sugar.' He grinned remorselessly. 'What guilt complexes? At a guess, they're all to do with your marriage...'

So he *had* been eavesdropping! There was a hot wash of colour in her cheeks. She was glad to hide behind her dark swath of hair as she poured boiling water into two white china mugs. Tipping milk into hers, she carried both back to the table, and clicked Daniel's down with scant grace in front of him.

'My marriage is none of your business,' she pointed out, 'and I think your time would be best spent delving into *your* psyche, prying into *your* past, don't you? Not snooping around overhearing conversations and poking your nose into *my* life!'

'Ouch. Firmly put in my place.' Daniel laughed shortly. The wry twist of his lips as he eyed her furious expression struck an answering chord somewhere inside her. Despite her fury, she found herself attempting a weak smile back.

'All these arguments, and we hardly know each other.' She raised her eyebrows mockingly.

'Yeah,' he agreed, deadpan, 'just think what hell we'd be if we *were* a couple.'

'Quite.' Carla found that she couldn't hold the cool, expressionless gaze. With a jerk, she switched her eyes to the view from the window. The silence intensified to the point where she could feel it clamping down on her, like an invisible vice. Then Daniel said easily, 'How long were you married?'

She sighed, then managed a slight laugh.

'Three years. You don't give up, do you? I think I've guessed your identity for you. Your interrogation skills have given you away. You're the real-life incarnation of my Detective Inspector Jack Tresawna!'

'Anything's possible. That's what's so unnerving.'

'What's so unnerving about being my fictional character come to life?'

Daniel grinned, but looked thoughtful.

'You're not suggesting I'm a myth? A psychic disturbance created by your overheated imagination, Carla?'

'You never know,' she said flippantly. 'Stranger stories have been recorded in this part of the world. Cornwall is full of myths...'

'But I'm flesh and blood,' he confirmed coolly, catching hold of her wrist across the table. 'Feel me...'

The physical contact jolted her. Sitting quite still, she stared down at the lean brown fingers circling her arm. She was trembling, she realised dimly. Surely something as simple as a hand on her arm couldn't make her feel like this? She stared at Daniel's hand, registering the well-shaped, strong-looking fingers, short, clean nails, the scattering of black hair at the wrist. His palm was warm, clasping the pulse-point in her wrist. Could he feel the faster rhythm? Feel her tension?

'Yes, I believe you,' she said hurriedly. She twisted away, pulled her wrist away, and stood up, before he could see the confusion in her eyes.

Just the touch of his hand on her arm had triggered a buried warmth in her stomach. Shivers of response in her thighs. A tingling in her breasts, thankfully well-protected from view beneath her voluminous blue jumper. But even more confusing was this unnerving sense of *déjà vu*. As if she'd met him before, somewhere, somehow, without remembering where or when. He seemed alien but familiar...

'The hint of strange, other-worldly happenings,' he was teasing calmly. 'Isn't that the style that made your Carl Julyan books well-known? Detective novels with a suggestion of the supernatural?'

'Yes. I suppose it is...' Dragging her frayed emotions together, she caught her breath, forced her thoughts back on to a logical course, furious with her own idiocy. She managed a commendably direct look. 'You seem remarkably alert and well-informed for a man suffering from memory-loss, you know.'

'Do you think I'm faking?' The cool challenge held a gleam of mockery. She shook her head.

'I didn't say that. What possible motive could you have for faking amnesia?'

'What indeed? I imagine that I'd have better methods of occupying my time.'

There was a pause. Carla collected the coffee-cups and began stacking dirty crockery into the dishwasher. Daniel's presence was like an invisible electric charge in the air behind her.

'What made you choose a male pseudonym?' He spoke calmly, breaking the silence. 'Does this have any connection with your habit of dressing like a boy?'

She paused as she stacked the last breakfast plate. Froze into stillness. Don't get angry, she urged herself silently. He obviously gets his kicks out of baiting people. Straightening up, she turned a cool, expressionless smile towards him.

'As a matter of fact, it probably does. I should have been a boy. Or so my parents always said.'

'Meaning that you always acted like one? Or that they would have preferred to have one?'

Carla gazed at him, her throat abruptly constricting. How often had she heard her father bemoan the fact that his longed-for son had turned out to be an unwanted daughter? Worse still, an unwanted daughter who didn't even grace the family snapshots with beauty and talent? She had a brief mental vision of herself growing up. Plump, plain, spotty, teeth in a brace until she was seventeen, hair stick-straight, that flat, uninteresting shade of dark brown which no amount of waving or styling seemed to transform.

'A bit of both,' she said aloud, with a casual shrug. 'And I'm sorry if you don't approve of my clothes.' She glanced down at her baggy denims,

and equally baggy jumper. So what if their bulk
and lack of cut did hide her figure? She hadn't the
least interest in her figure. Catching a glimpse of
her face, pale and devoid of make-up, in the mirror
over the sink, she looked quickly away. Dressed like
a boy? Did this horrible man have to be so intensely personal all the time? Couldn't he just make
polite conversation and mind his manners?

'One thing you're certainly not is a diplomat!'
She grinned, determinedly retrieving her poise. 'But
whatever your profession you're definitely an
amateur psychologist!'

'It doesn't take a psychologist to detect that
you're unhappy with your femininity, Carla.' It was
drawled softly. Suppressing the urge to throw
something at him, she shrugged again, fighting an
annoying heat in her cheeks.

'I'm a full-time writer, not a . . . a photographic
model. And you're wrong. Whatever I am, I'm
perfectly happy with it, thanks. Now, can I get you
some more coffee?'

He shook his head, and then winced as if he
wished he hadn't.

'Do I gather this place used to be a farm? Before
your husband died?'

'Yes . . . this was one of several places my father
owned and rented out. He gave it to us as a wedding
present. Silver was mined here once.' She was so
relieved to have the spotlight temporarily off herself,
she was gabbling nervously. 'Then it was a dairy

farm. Then beef and vegetables. We had a few horses until...until my husband died...'

'So your husband ran the farm, while you wrote books?'

'Yes. Although he didn't really enjoy being a farmer...' In fact, he'd run the farm right down, she reflected.

'What did he want to do?'

'He wanted to own his own company, be the successful businessman. He bought into a business once, before we married. But he had a bad experience with a back-stabbing friend, and lost out... Look, would you please stop?'

'Stop what?'

'Grilling me about my life!'

'There's very little point in your grilling me about mine,' he pointed out, 'since I can't remember a damned thing about it.'

'True...' Despite her irritation, she felt a pang of sympathy.

'What are you so defensive about, anyway?' he wanted to know, his eyes cool on her hesitant expression.

'Nothing. I'll complete my entire life story if it amuses you,' she went on calmly. 'I went to an all-girls' boarding-school in Somerset, followed by an English degree at Exeter. I then couldn't find a job, but, since I'd already decided all I wanted to do was write novels, it was probably a blessing in disguise. My father was chairman of a big international farm machinery company and he and my mother were abroad a lot. My late husband's parents were friends of my parents, through the farming connection. That's how he and I knew each other...'

'And you fell in love and got married.'

She turned her back on him, and stared out of the window. The spell of fine weather was continuing. The pale sun shone on the wide sweep of bay. The sea shimmered with a million tiny reflections.

'Of course. What else?'

'People have various reasons for marrying,' Daniel said calmly. 'I just wondered what yours was.'

Carla felt as if that X-ray vision was somehow penetrating the back of her head, sorting mercilessly through her jumbled thoughts. She swung round and faced him. She felt tense as a reed under the searching appraisal, and now she was angry. Really angry.

'OK. I realise you were listening in on my conversation with Becky...'

'I couldn't help overhearing the tail-end of it. It sounded to me as if you were putting yourself down.'

Carla drew a deep breath, and glared at her tormentor.

'I realise you've time on your hands, and apparently nothing better to do than amuse yourself at my expense...' Her heart was thudding. Two angry flags of colour darkened her cheeks. She was painfully aware of his eyes searching her face, moving slowly and consideringly over her from head to toe.

'Hey... I'm sorry.' His voice was cool. 'You're right. I was going to say that your husband sounded like an insensitive bastard. But maybe I'm one too.'

She swallowed.

'Well, you said it.'

Daniel stood up, stretched his shoulders slightly. His dark face was wry.

'Thanks for breakfast, Carla. I think I'll go for a walk.'

She found herself staring at him in consternation, in spite of her suppressed anger.

'I don't think you should go alone...'

A sardonic gleam sharpened the cool green. 'Don't worry, I'll steer clear of the lower cliff-path.'

'Even so...' Why was she feeling so guilty? But if he was still getting headaches, and still suffering from amnesia, surely he shouldn't be left to his own devices for too long?

'Even so?' he teased gently. 'I've been discharged from hospital. I'm feeling fitter by the hour. The police haven't managed to pin any unsolved murders on me yet. And making idle conversation with you seems to be fraught with unexploded time bombs. I need some air.'

'Of course.' Turning away, she closed the dishwasher with a controlled click, and briefly shut her eyes. 'I must get back to my study. I'm in the middle of a book...'

'In that case, I'll keep out of your way.'

There was no expression in his voice, but she found herself swinging round abruptly.

'If you need anything, let me know.'

'Thanks.' He shot her a cool smile and strolled towards the door. 'And stop looking so worried. You haven't been officially appointed my keeper, have you?'

'No.'

'See you later.'

When he'd gone, she hung on to the worktop fiercely for a few seconds, then felt almost limp with reaction. She watched him disappear across the gravelled yard, and into the cottage, his loose-limbed, rangy walk holding her gaze, in spite of her anger.

Breathing deeply, she forced herself to finish the routine morning jobs, before marching purposefully into her study and slamming the door shut.

Here was her sanctuary, her haven. Here was the place she'd retreated to when things had got unbearable during her marriage. She switched on the word processor, slotted in the disk, and tried to immerse herself in the complexities of her current plot...

For once, her characters seemed to elude her. Inspector Jack Tresawna, the drily spoken Celt with the passion for local history and a habit of accidentally tapping in to another dimension in the course of his investigations, somehow lacked any substance in her mind. Instead, all she could see as she concentrated on her story was the dark, rather harsh image of Daniel's face. In place of Jack Tresawna's piercing blue eyes she kept seeing Daniel's equally piercing green. Sea-green, and amused. Watchful and intelligent, beneath those straight dark eyebrows, and above lean, slightly hollow cheeks. Tresawna's firm mouth blurred into Daniel's well-shaped, slightly quirky lips.

Carla sat motionless at her desk, staring into space, the two images melting together in the most exasperating way in her mind's eye. It was almost as if Daniel and Jack Tresawna had merged into the same man. Which was the craziest idea she'd had so far, she lashed herself impatiently. But the lunatic notion refused to go. It totally blocked her ability to write. The intricacies of her plot defeated her. The multi-layered strands waiting to be neatly unravelled stayed stubbornly tangled.

Finally, she abandoned the attempt. Fetching her waxed jacket from the hook in the hall, she thrust her feet into wellingtons and set off towards the coastal path at an impatient pace. When she couldn't write, walking often proved therapeutic. It was a cool, breezy November morning. The sun still defied a depressing weather forecast and was steadily gilding the green and blue landscape. It would soon be December, but it had been such a mild autumn, there were even more wisps of tamarisk still blooming, lacy pink on the feathery bushes. The deeper pink of a few late-flowering wild valerian dotted the hedges as she made her way through to the open cliff-top.

The lower path was blocked, but she took the higher one, which wound round behind banks of gorse and bracken, and eventually looped back towards the cliff edge.

Then she saw Daniel. He was sitting not far above the spot where he'd fallen, his Barbour jacket spread out beneath him, elbows resting on bent knees, hands thrust into his hair, staring fixedly out to sea. He looked so isolated, so frustrated and alone, her heart seemed to squeeze idiotically in her chest.

Drawn like a magnet, she found herself steering her steps down towards him. He heard her approaching, and slowly turned to watch her.

'Hello again,' she said brightly, stopping a few feet away.

'Hello.' He sounded abrupt, then smiled ruefully. 'I thought you had a book to finish? Did you feel obliged to make sure I hadn't fallen over the cliff again?'

'No. I couldn't concentrate. Walking helps...' She hesitated. Pride dictated that she exchange pleasantries and then continue on her way. But something about that lonely aura he'd projected kept her rooted to the spot. She heard herself saying, 'Do you mind if I join you?'

'Be my guest.' He moved to the edge of the spread Barbour, and after a few seconds' inner battle she forced herself to sit down, at the furthest edge away from him. Feeling prim and prudish, she sensed his humorous glance. She kept her eyes on the horizon.

'I'm not scintillating company this morning,' he added. 'I've been sitting here staring at St Michael's Mount out there, wondering why the hell I can't remember who I am!'

'Getting angry about it won't help. Stress could make it worse.'

'What a wise woman you are, Carla.' The mockery was tempered with a wry smile. The sudden glimmer of warmth in his eyes made her look quickly away again.

'At least you know that's St Michael's Mount,' she pointed out.

'Yup. Which tells me I've been in this part of the world before.'

'So it does!' She turned to him, eyes alight. 'And slowly but surely it will all come back, Daniel.'

'I'm sure you're right. If I can survive the wait.'

'Are you a naturally impatient person?'

He shrugged. 'Impatient is maybe the wrong word. Active. I'd say I feel like I'm naturally active. I get the feeling I'm used to a lot of challenge in my life. Mental and physical.'

She gazed at him, her brain whirring in fascination.

'Let's just run over everything we know about you again,' she suggested firmly. 'You're roughly... thirtyish, I'd say.'

'Is that meant to be compliment or insult?'

'Neither,' she said crisply. 'Let's try to keep this impersonal, shall we?'

'Yes, ma'am.'

She shot him a vexed look. Couldn't he take her efforts to help a little more seriously?

'You don't have an accent. Apart from an Oxford-style accent, that is. Which suggests you're well-educated. You seem intelligent . . .'

'Can my ego cope with all this?'

'You were walking east along the coast path, from the Penzance direction. You were wearing denims, checked brushed-cotton shirt, brown leather walking-shoes, this green jumper and the Barbour jacket we're sitting on. On your wrist you were wearing an eighteen-carat-gold Rolex Oyster Chronometer which the police seemed pretty sure was worth a small fortune. In the pocket of your shirt you had a hundred pounds in twenty-pound notes. And that cryptic note from "R". Is that it? Is there anything else at all?'

He slanted a ruthless grin at her. 'You missed the dark green socks and the navy striped boxer-shorts.'

'Are they significant?' She would *not* blush.

'Strangely enough, they could be,' he said expressionlessly. 'The boxer-shorts had a label from an up-market New York store. Not your run-of-the-mill boxer-shorts at all.'

'Yes. Well, that's interesting. You've either been to America, or you've got a sweet old American aunty who sends you American boxer-shorts for your birthday, maybe?'

'Right.'

She let out her breath in a rush, and shook her head.

'This is hopeless,' she said flatly. 'I'm clearly wasting my time.'

'Not at all. I appreciate the effort you're making,' he affirmed nonchalantly, 'but, like you said, getting impatient doesn't help. I can't rush my memory back.'

'Sorry. I am impatient, I admit,' she confessed with a short laugh. 'One of my many failings.'

'Don't put yourself down again, Carla,' he advised, standing up. 'If you want my opinion, I'd say you don't have nearly as many failings as the rest of us mortals. Angelic verging on the martyred would be my verdict . . .'

'Is *that* supposed to be a compliment?'

She began to jump to her feet beside him. She caught her foot in the sleeve of his jacket, and, losing balance, she stumbled against him, felt him stagger slightly under the impact of her weight. Her upper arms were firmly clamped in supporting hands as he retrieved the situation. Speechless, she tried to jerk shyly away, but he held her still. She looked up, and met his shadowed gaze.

'Yes, it was,' he said quietly, 'of sorts . . .'

There was silence between them suddenly. Carla opened her mouth to say something, but no sound came out. She was mesmerised by the expression in his eyes. Her throat tight, her heart thudding, she began shaking her head, unsure why.

'Carla...' It wasn't a question exactly, more a stifled warning. Then slowly, and with almost exploratory caution, he bent his head and gently kissed her parted lips.

CHAPTER THREE

ALMOST simultaneously, they jumped apart as if they'd been stung. Daniel was gazing at Carla with blank, unfathomable eyes, then he squeezed his eyes shut as if trying to block out what he saw.

She felt electrified. Every nerve-end tingling. Her heart pounding. Abruptly she thrust her shaky hands through her wind-blown hair, then clutched her arms around her defensively.

'Why did you do that?' she demanded huskily.

He'd opened his eyes again. The sea-green gaze still held no recognisable emotion. Not anger, nor remorse, nor even mockery.

'I'm not sure,' he said flatly, expelling his breath on a short sharp burst. 'It wasn't a good idea.'

'No. It wasn't!' Her response was automatic, but inside she vaguely recognised a surge of conflict. Unidentifiable emotions seemed to be scudding through her as haphazardly as the clouds across the sky. If he touched her again, if he touched his mouth to hers again, she didn't know how she'd feel...

'Maybe we'd better get one thing straight,' she added frostily, dropping her arms and thrusting her hands into her pockets. 'I'm not a...a frustrated widow, yearning for sexual fulfilment...'

One dark brow tilted as he watched her.

'I'm sure you're not.'

'And let's face it,' she persisted, her anger hardening as she detected that teasing glint, 'you could be *anyone*!'

He nodded slowly. 'Anyone in expensive American boxer-shorts,' he amended. The wicked gleam had sharpened to real amusement.

Furious with his seemingly limitless sense of humour, she swung round and began walking back towards the house. He followed her.

'What is really annoying me,' she went on, aware of him walking calmly beside her but not trusting herself to look at him, 'is this attitude of yours...'

'You're saying I have an attitude problem?'

'You treat me as if... as if I'd *willed* you to fall off the cliff on my doorstep!' she bit out on a low, angry laugh. 'As if I especially *wanted* you to be here...'

'Are you trying to be rational?'

'Will you please stop poking fun?' she burst out, stopping at the door to the house, and almost tripping over Moppy, who'd padded up to wind himself round her legs in greeting. 'I'm trying to tell you that I may have offered you the cottage, as a place to recuperate, but I'm not offering anything else. OK?'

'That's not true,' he pointed out good-naturedly. 'You're definitely offering a diversion to sitting alone waiting for total recall.'

'Well, I'm glad I'm so entertaining for you! But I've got feelings too, you know...'

'Carla...'

'Just because you're bored and... and disorientated, it doesn't justify using me as an entertaining oddity to while away your time——'

'I'm sorry...'

'—keeping your wits sharpened by poking your nose into my private life, interrogating me about my past, my marriage, my motives in offering to help you...'

'Carla, will you calm down?' Stepping closer, he put his arms around her, and pulled her against him. Shocked into awareness, she dimly realised that she was crying. Shivering with reaction, she didn't fight him. His arms tightened a little, and she found her face against the rough wool of his sweater, the back of her head clasped in a firm hand as he held her hard against him. 'It's OK, I'm sorry...' he murmured, a soothing quality in his voice. Feeling absurdly childlike, she shuddered to suppress a sob, and reluctantly allowed his warmth and strength to filter through to her. Only the comforting feeling lasted no more than a few seconds. After that came the disturbing battle of emotions. Warm, twisting sensations deep inside her breasts and stomach, an unfamiliar tremor of response somewhere in the region of her thighs...

He smelled good. Very clean, very male. Her head swam, and she tensed.

'Better?' He'd released her a little, holding her away from him to look down at her face.

'Yes...' She had to say something, anything to deflect those piercing eyes from reading her thoughts. 'Yes, I'm fine. And it's me who should apologise,' she went on in a rush. 'I'm being touchy and defensive. Over-emotional. Sorry...'

There was a wry gleam of humour in his gaze. But somehow she felt as if she'd sensed something deeper in him, something beyond the habitual mockery. Something which seemed to her a thousand times more sensitive and understanding than Rufus could ever have been, even if he'd lived to a ripe old age...

It occurred to her, like a fragmented notion out of nowhere, that this man could well be married and have children. There was every chance that he was, that he had...and if he had she somehow felt sure he'd be a good husband and father...

She stepped away from him, appalled at how much this mental picture hurt her. Her thoughts flicked involuntarily to her own bitterly unhappy marriage...

Rufus had been horrified at the idea of children. Children would get in the way of his 'game-plan', as he'd put it...it hadn't taken long to realise that her husband had a self-centred streak as well as that deep strain of bitterness and resentment. It had meant that he'd never managed to come to terms with any of the set-backs in his life. First, the loss of his family wealth, suddenly finding that cushion snatched away, and then in his career, his confidence knocked out of him by his disagreement with his business partner... That unfortunate tendency towards self-pity had transformed the latter set-back into a body-blow. He'd never recovered from it...

She'd never met that arrogant ex-partner of his. But, despite her disillusion with her husband, she decided that she felt a degree of resentment towards Leo Tremayne as well... Whatever the rights and wrongs of it all, whatever Rufus's probable guilt in the matter, Leo Tremayne had proved the final straw, embittered Rufus, ruined Rufus's life, and indirectly, therefore, hers as well...

'I have a suggestion,' Daniel was saying drily. 'Why don't we both stop apologising to each other, and start all over again? Do you want some amazingly good coffee?'

'Well...'

'Come into my cottage, and I'll brew you some,' he offered nonchalantly. 'And I promise to stop offending you, if you promise to stop taking offence?'

It was no good. She had to laugh.

'Sounds a fair deal.'

'It does, doesn't it?'

Daniel evidently had experience of brewing coffee. The quantities of the grounds to boiling water in the cafetière were the secret, he informed her with a grin. Carla had to admit his expertise produced a very drinkable cup of coffee.

'Drinkable? This is aromatic perfection,' he told her, throwing a log on to the fire he'd evidently lit that morning, and sitting opposite her.

'At the risk of taking offence again, are you implying that the cup of coffee I provided at breakfast fell way below your standards?'

Daniel eyed her, with a quirk of his lips.

'At the risk of giving offence, yes.'

'Lord, but you must be hell for someone to live with!' She sighed with mock-sympathy. 'Not all of us are coffee freaks. A cup of instant is fine for me.'

'What an unrepentant philistine. I'm obviously wasting my talents on you.'

'No, really, it's very good.' She grinned. And so was sharing morning coffee with Daniel, she reflected with a stab of panic. Catching the answering gleam in Daniel's green eyes, her pulses began to race all over again. Those lazy, hypnotic eyes. That slow, devastating smile. Warmth engulfed her, and she stiffened involuntarily. This was ridiculous, unthinkable . . . of all the hundreds of reasons why she shouldn't get emotionally involved with another man, not one of them came close to the folly of involvement with this man. He was a stranger. Even more than a stranger, he was a totally unknown quantity, even to himself. He could be a priest or a thief, a wanted criminal or a happily married family man, with a distraught wife sitting by a telephone right this moment, wondering where he was . . . maybe someone with the initial 'R' . . . ?

The lurch of realisation made her feel slightly sick with dismay. But when she flicked a tense glance at him she saw that he'd closed his eyes, leaning his head back on the high-backed wing-chair. The blank weariness on his face caught her off-guard. He looked shattered, she registered guiltily. Despite the harsh, masculine features, the tough air about him, he looked so haggard she felt ashamed of her touchy self-absorption. And equally confused by her stupidity.

She felt warmth creep up to her cheeks at the thought of his kiss, however brief and dismissive it might have been. She'd felt so...so swept up by her response...however quickly he'd condemned it as a bad idea...

She pressed her fingers to her mouth involuntarily. Surely she wasn't about to make a complete fool of herself by succumbing to sexual attraction, with a total stranger? By allowing this unknown man to succeed where all others had failed?

Daniel opened his eyes and stared at her. For a few seconds, he looked as if he didn't even recognise her.

'Are you all right?' she said huskily.

'Yes, I'm all right.' His mouth tilted wryly. 'I'm just mentally kicking at the barriers. It's like being in prison. For something you didn't do.'

'You must be feeling so frustrated.' She nodded, with a surge of sympathy. 'But someone will notice you're missing from their lives! Very soon.'

'Maybe I'm a loner,' he suggested flatly. 'Maybe there's no one out there to miss me?'

She stared at him, slowly shaking her head.

'No. You're much too...' She'd been about to say 'attractive', then bit her lip. That sounded too incriminating. Frantically she searched for a better word. 'Too *interested* in people to be that much of a loner.'

'You think so?'

She nodded briskly. 'I know so. Look at the way you've been compiling a case-history on me.'

'A case-history?' he echoed, amused again. 'You think I could be a doctor, maybe?'

'Whatever you are, I'd say you're not a social pariah,' she concluded, with a slight laugh. 'And I'd say you're fairly attractive to women.' There, she'd said it, without making it sound like a personal statement. Gaining confidence, she pursued her theme. 'Look at the way my friend Becky took to you, within minutes of introduction. I mean, Becky's happily married, but I can tell she liked you. Hence the rather embarrassing dinner invite!'

'I wasn't embarrassed.' Daniel's humorous gaze had narrowed on her slightly flushed face. 'You were.'

'Well, obviously. I mean, we hardly know each other. And it's not as if...'

'Not as if we're friends, or anything?' he finished for her.

'Exactly.'

'Lodger and landlady, in fact.'

'Quite. Oh, I forgot to mention...' She glanced down at her hands, before ploughing on doggedly, 'The cottage is booked for a pre-Christmas holiday let in three weeks' time. I hope that won't be too soon for...'

'Don't worry, Carla,' he assured her, eyes grave, 'I'll be long gone by then. And I'm sorry for kissing you. It was a moment's... aberration.'

'Right.' She swallowed on a sudden tight feeling in her throat, and abruptly drained her coffee-cup. She avoided his eyes. That was the most sensible thing she'd heard all morning. Why did her stomach feel flat and hollow?

'Well, I must go and do some work, or I'll have my agent breathing down my neck muttering deadlines...'

'And I might stroll into the village, buy myself a newspaper,' Daniel said lightly. 'Check to see if there's some frantic search going on for me.'

'Good idea,' she forced out crisply. 'See you later. But don't overdo thc exercise—head injuries take time to heal.'

'Yes, ma'am,' he said with deceptive meekness. She felt his eyes follow her as she left. It was like a warm shiver down her spine.

Carla had hoped that her writing might go slightly better during the rest of the morning. But when she sat down again in the privacy of her study she was overwhelmed by delayed reaction.

She'd made a big mistake, she'd realised. She should have had more sense. She'd been mad to offer him the cottage...

But how in the world could she have known how she would begin to feel about someone she'd only just met? Especially someone suffering from memory-loss, someone who had another life silently waiting for him, like a potential time-bomb?

Agitated and furious, she ran upstairs to her bedroom and forced herself to inspect her reflection dispassionately in the long pine mirror on the wall. Look at yourself, she whipped herself angrily. Even if he were free to embark on some emotional involvement, do you honestly imagine he would choose *you*?

Her track record on relationships was ghastly. Those plump and plain years at school hadn't been the only pointers to a lack of sex appeal. Her parents, especially Dad, had made no secret of their preference for a boy. Their only child had been a girl, and Carla hadn't even been a beautiful girl, one Mummy could dress in pretty pink dresses to rival the other little party-goers. She'd been tall for her age, overweight, awkward and clumsy, but it had been Dad's scathing disapproval which clinched her insecurity...

Hardly knowing what she was doing, she marched over to the wardrobe and flung it open, gazing with distaste at the familiar assortment of clothes. How long was it since she'd treated herself to a full shopping spree, pampered herself with a new outfit?

Tearing the outsized sweater over her head, kicking off the baggy jeans and trainers, she rummaged in her lingerie drawer for a satin bra and matching French knickers. She slipped them on in place of her cotton ones. Then, almost fiercely, she pulled a calf-length, gathered black velvet skirt from her wardrobe, along with a diaphanous black voile shirt.

The skirt was one of her secret favourites, discovered in a shop selling clothes from Asia, on one of her few trips up to London to meet her agent. It had a braid of heavy, ethnic-style beading in silver around the hem and along the wide cummerbund waistband. The shirt was cut loose and floaty from a gathered yoke. It was very see-through—it needed a black 'body' underneath—but for the moment, in the privacy of her room, she contented herself with the slinky honey-coloured lingerie.

She'd worn the black outfit only once, two Christmases ago, her concession to looking feminine and elegant for a party, but at the same time sticking to her own rather eccentric ideas of dressing up. She slipped on the skirt and shrugged on the blouse, which draped softly across the firm fullness of her breasts. Then she added lace-up Victorian leather ankle-boots.

Her reflection in the mirror seemed to mock her, even so. She certainly looked . . . different. More feminine, but rather off-beat. Rather pale and dramatic, in fact. It needed the delicate ethnic silver jewellery which was another of her secret favourites. Delving into her rarely used jewel-box, she clipped on dangly silver earrings, shaped like new moons with pendant stars, and fastened a heavy Celtic cross around her neck.

Then she looked at herself again. It was silly to picture herself still as plump. Her figure could probably now be described as...statuesque? She grimaced, mocking herself. That was the polite description for tallish, large-busted females, wasn't it? But her waist and hips were slim, her legs long and reasonably shapely. Stepping closer to the mirror, she examined her pale face and wind-blown dark hair. Slowly, she sat down at her dressing-table, picked up her brush and smoothed her hair into a thick, neat, shining bob, curving just below her jawline. Then, casually, she picked up her make-up bag and stroked on some slate-blue eyeshadow which accentuated the purplish-blue of her eyes, fluffed on a faint trace of blusher, coloured the full curve of her mouth with a deeper brownish-pink lipstick.

As a final antidote to her negative state of mind, she sprayed a soft musk-based perfume on her pulse-points, and slid some silver Gemini rings on her fingers. Once again, she reappraised the girl in the mirror...

Not bad. Better.

But she was living in cloud-cuckoo land if she imagined she would hold any attraction for a man like Daniel.

And what *was* 'a man like Daniel'? she reminded herself impatiently. Why on earth should she imagine he was any different from all the rest? And how could she be so feather-brained even to think of finding him attractive, knowing nothing about him, knowing he knew nothing about himself?

What an idiot she was, dressing up and fantasising, just because one man had accidentally touched a hidden chord inside her...

Overcome with shame and self-disgust, she was about to change back into denims and sweater when the telephone rang. Becky's voice came brightly over the line.

'Carla! Hi, how's it going?'

'Fine...' she lied carefully. 'No thanks to you, though!'

'How come?'

'Your dinner invitation wasn't exactly tactful,' Carla reproached, 'bearing in mind the man's a total stranger, and you'd come to warn me to be careful to lock my doors at night!'

'He was just so *gorgeous*,' Becky admitted with a laugh, 'I was sort of bowled over! I couldn't help myself! Do say you'll come, Carla—that's why I was ringing. Come tomorrow night—and bring him along!'

'You make him sound like a dog or something...!'

'Oh, definitely not! Carla, I haven't seen a man with so much . . . *charisma* for years! Darling, he's amazing! Go on, say yes. It will do you good! And, let's face it, there's a distinct shortage of eligible men in Penuthna!'

'Has it occurred to you that Daniel may not be *eligible*?' Carla declared bluntly, blushing as she recalled her own thoughts a few minutes earlier. 'He's most likely married with an amazing, charismatic, gorgeous wife and half a dozen equally amazing, charismatic, gorgeous children . . .'

'Unlikely, since nobody's sending out passionate SOSs for him,' Becky put in, with justice.

'Well, there you are, then. Points to something jolly sinister about the man, doesn't it? And in any case I'm busy writing. I'm not in the market for being paired off, Becky!'

'Think about it . . . sinister or not, I'm going to ask Daniel anyway. Let's face it, the village needs to show a bit of welcome and hospitality! The poor man needs all the support he can get!'

'Becky . . .'

There was a knocking from downstairs.

'Hang on, there's someone at the front door.'

'I'll see you at eight tomorrow night, then,' Becky said decisively, and hung up, leaving Carla glaring in frustration at the receiver.

'Carla . . . ?' Daniel's voice came from the hall. She'd left the front door unlocked.

Flustered and preoccupied, she swiftly darted downstairs, and almost bumped into Daniel's tall form at the bottom. It wasn't until she saw the slight widening of his eyes that she remembered what she was wearing.

Heat swept through her as she registered his reaction.

'You look nice,' he commented mildly, his cool green gaze moving from the lace-up boots, up over the velvet skirt and lingering with slight disbelief on the see-through blouse. 'Are you going somewhere special?'

'No...I...' Frantically, she kept her poise. 'I...often dress up when I'm writing. It makes me feel more...businesslike!'

'Oh, I sec.' His wry expression said far more than words. She was nearly dying of embarrassment.

'Did you want something?' she demanded furiously.

'Yes. I thought I might try to refresh what's left of my memory on your Inspector Jack Tresawna,' Daniel said lightly, eyeing the bookcases visible in her study, in the alcove by the fire. 'If you don't mind?'

'No, of course not...' She followed his gaze to the bookshelves, and marched self-consciously into her study. 'I'll lend you the whole lot if you think it would help?'

'Who knows? I'm grasping at straws for the moment.' He took the first few handed to him, and glanced curiously at the covers. '*The Moon's Men*— I remember this one,' he said slowly, turning it over in his hand, gazing at the shiny cover picture with hooded black figures hunched against a dark, moonlit, wind-swept hillside. 'It's weird. How selective this memory-loss seems to be...'

'Nothing in the newspapers, then?' she queried shortly.

'Not a thing. Maybe I'm an alien, beamed down from outer space?'

'That would explain a lot.' She smiled back, in spite of herself.

'It certainly would,' he agreed. He was looking at her in a way that unsettled her so much, she reached for the edge of her desk for support. 'It would explain this sense of being in limbo. Floating somewhere between life and death...'

'Is that how you feel?'

'From time to time. Having no identity is...' he frowned, then grinned rather bleakly '...limiting.'

She nodded, staring at him.

'I sympathise. Although there've been plenty of times in my life when I've wanted to trade mine for a new one.'

Daniel met her gaze, a thoughtful expression in his eyes.

'Is it that bad, being Carla Julyan?'

She shrugged slightly. Suddenly she was aware of getting out of her depth. But she wasn't quite sure how to extricate herself. Was there some quality in Daniel that inspired honesty? Almost mesmerised, she heard herself saying, 'There were times in my teens when I'd have given anything to be a boy!'

He tilted an eyebrow. Putting the books down on the edge of her green leather desk-top, he propped himself against the desk beside her. She could smell the fresh air on him, from his walk to the village. The denim-clad thighs compressed against the desk bulged with tightly toned muscle. She felt her heart lurch and skip a beat, and moved jerkily away. She could hardly breathe when he came so close.

'But not so much now?' he queried softly. 'How old are you, Carla?'

'Twenty-five. Daniel, I really don't——'

'Hey, don't get so uptight,' he suggested calmly. 'You're not built like you're meant to be a boy.'

'I have to go upstairs and change . . .' she began breathlessly, but as she moved past him he stopped her. Catching her hand, he pulled her firmly round to face him. In the charged silence, she could hear her own heart thudding, she could feel his warmth. It was comforting and threatening at the same time. She was starting to shiver.

'You're trembling. Don't look so terrified,' he advised. 'I'm not about to take advantage of your lone status here, Carla. Whoever I am, I don't get the feeling I'm an escaped scx offender . . .'

'Daniel, please . . .' Her voice was husky. She felt desperate with shame, humiliation at the way he was making her feel, the way she knew she shouldn't be feeling . . .

'Just don't deny your beauty,' he told her, his voice slightly huskier too. 'Don't suppress your femininity. You're a lovely woman, Carla. You've got the face of an angel. The body of a siren. Don't waste your life trying to be something you're not...'

Her whole body was hot and shivery, half embarrassed, half engulfed with a mystifying desire she'd never experienced.

'You're talking rubbish,' she whispered angrily. 'Do you really think I'm gullible enough to go for that kind of line?'

'What kind of line?' The green gaze was hypnotic, but a spark of anger gleamed there. 'Do you think I'm trying to come on to you?'

'I don't know what you're trying to do...'

His eyes locked with hers, sea-green with stormy blue. Anger began to transmute. The turmoil inside her grew so great, she could almost hear it roaring in her ears, like the distant roar of the sea at the bottom of the ocean, fathoms deep. But inside the turmoil, at its centre, was a restless longing.

With a muffled curse, he jerked her closer, held her to him. The sensation of his hard fingers on her back, through the fine voile of the blouse, was so intense, she gasped as if he'd burned her.

'Carla...oh, sweet heaven, Carla...' He caught her shoulders, gave her a slight, despairing shake, and then dropped his head, out of control, and sought her trembling lips, kissing her with a hunger that, unbelievably, matched her own...

CHAPTER FOUR

AFTERWARDS, Carla was never sure who halted the spiral of passion. But she found herself free, her hands on Daniel's shoulders, floundering up from a hot darkness. Daniel steadied her as she stumbled, and she almost fell against him again. He was breathing hard, his pupils dilated. And even though she'd merely been held closely in his arms, and kissed with an expertise which left her dizzy, she felt as if he'd touched her all over. A pulse darted erratically in her throat. Her breasts felt swollen with a sensitivity she'd never felt before. Her stomach and her legs were melting, hollow and empty with unexplained longing...

'You don't know what I'm trying to do to you?' he murmured grimly. 'It's the other way around, Carla. Are you a witch?'

'A *witch*?' she countered, shakily. She was aware of his eyes, narrowed, but unashamedly inspecting the jut of her breasts beneath the diaphanous black blouse as he held her away from him. 'Daniel, believe me, I'm no witch...'

'This is crazy,' he said, half to himself. But his voice was still thick with desire, and his hand shook as he carefully traced the curve of her cheek, then dropped his finger to outline the swell of her breast.

She tensed, catching her breath involuntarily. He switched the sensual caress to her back, stroking around to explore the smooth, narrow planes of her shoulder-blades, encountering the catch on her bra with an infinitesimal pause before flicking it open.

'No...' It was a desperate whisper, but she didn't move. Inside, she was in a torment of self-doubt. This couldn't be happening to her, Carla Julyan, at midday, in her own study...

'It's OK,' he whispered hoarsely. 'I just want to look at you...'

'Daniel...' She was trembling now, from head to toe.

'You're exquisite, Carla...'

She shut her eyes, rigid with self-consciousness. The slither of the fabric told her she was exposed to him, her breasts naked. The rough catch in his voice was as erotic as a physical caress.

'Open your eyes,' he ordered quietly. His hands were warm on her ribcage, beneath the jut of her breasts. Shivering, she did as he said, lifting her eyes to meet the scorch of his gaze.

'Now look at yourself,' he added unevenly. 'See? Whatever your feelings about your womanhood, Carla, you can't hide how desirable you are.'

'I don't want to...' She could hardly believe she'd said it. Tentatively, driven by some inner urge too strong to control, she reached up her hands to cup his face. The plaster on his temple obstructed her sensory investigation, but she carefully stroked the thickness of his dark hair, wonderingly, lost in the strange magic of the moment. 'Kiss me again...' she added on a rush of shyness, pulling him down, pulling his head down to hers...

It was like leaping into the dark. No rules, no safety net, just blotting out reality, throwing herself into the swirling blindness of raw new emotions. When his lips had traced a path from her mouth, down her arched throat, over the satin swell of her breast to one acutely sensitive nipple, she twined her arms round him, and shut her eyes. A million shivers brushed the surface of her skin.

'You really want this?' he demanded, in a hoarse, incredulous whisper. But she couldn't answer. She was adrift, out of control on a shuddering torrent of need. 'Carla, sweetheart...' It was a low groan, rough and increasingly demanding.

'Do you want me?' she heard herself whisper, trembling in his arms. 'Do you really want me?'

Daniel hauled himself back from the brink with visible self-control. Shocked back to reality, she opened her eyes, heat flooding her.

'Oh, yes,' he assured her unevenly, pulling her blouse round her and folding her into his arms, so that she could feel the strong hammering of his heart against hers, 'I really want you. But we'd better put the brakes on, Carla. Or I won't be answerable for my actions...'

White-faced, slightly dazed, she pushed herself away and stood staring at him for a few seconds, while the full impact of her foolishness slammed

into her. Then, with a choked cry, she turned and
ran from the room, dashing to the stairs and up to
her bedroom.

There, door shut, leaning against the panelled
pine with thudding heart and racing pulses, she
stood for a long time, striving for calm.

Her bedroom, like the rest of the farmhouse, and
even the cottage she'd renovated, was furnished
with the glowing colours and ethnic patterns she
liked to surround herself with. Vibrant dark greens,
reds, spice colours and golds. She tried to draw
comfort from its feeling of welcome and warmth.
She tried to rationalise her actions to herself...

But all she could think of was the ecstasy of
Daniel's touch, the wild surge of joy in her veins
when he kissed her. How could she feel like this,
with someone she'd only just met? Someone she
barely knew? When her whole life to date had
lacked that elusive spark with any other man?

Levering herself slowly away from the door, she
went to the mirror, stared at herself. Flushed cheeks
and brilliant eyes gazed back. Her breasts were still
heaving as she struggled to slow her breathing. She
shuddered in dismay. What had possessed her to
reveal her feelings just now? What had possessed
her to *have* those feelings? To let herself go, with
such wildly incriminating honesty?

She bit her lip painfully, gazing at the full,
rounded jut of her breasts beneath the fine black
voile. She'd never seen herself like this, she realised
with a jolt. Her nipples were tightly pointed, the

aureolae contracted in shivery arousal, deep crimson buds against the milky white of her skin. The memory of his lips against her made her clench her teeth in anguish, shutting her eyes.

She'd have to face him again. Was it possible to die of shame? What would he think of her?

She didn't even know what to think of herself...

Mercifully, she was spared the immediate embarrassment of facing Daniel. When she marched downstairs, safely ensconced in her normal clothes, he'd gone back to his cottage. Back at her desk, she used every scrap of self-discipline she could find to lose herself in her writing. This time she found that it worked. Maybe her subconscious mind was only too glad to take over. Maybe she was only too thankful to blot out what had just happened with Daniel...

A pang of hunger eventually brought a brief dilemma. It was rather late for lunch—half-past two in fact. Would Daniel have got himself something? Should she make him a snack, take it across? She had offered to help with meals, during his recovery. It would seem immature to ignore him totally, just because she felt like entering a nunnery.

Steeling her nerve, she loaded up a tray with two cheese rolls, a bowl of salad, and a jug of freshly squeezed orange juice. This thing was better tackled head-on, she told herself firmly. They were two mature adults. She could handle the embarrassment if he could...

Daniel was stretched out in the wing-chair. It was dim in the cottage, even in daylight. Now that the sun had gone behind the clouds, a lamp on a side-table was lighting the book he was reading. A log still smouldered and glowed on the fire. The scene in the cottage had such a home-coming quality about it, she blinked for an instant, thrown off balance again.

'Sorry to disturb this peaceful scene——' she laughed nervously '—but I'm sure regular meal-times must be essential for amnesia-sufferers?'

'Undoubtedly.' He'd laid down the book as she appeared at the door, and glanced at his watch. 'Is this lunchtime around here?' He was looking at her with such wry caution, she felt herself stiffen defensively as she placed the tray on the coffee-table.

'Not usually. I got engrossed in my writing.'

'Don't worry. If I'd felt hungry I'd have fixed myself something. I see you've abandoned your professional writing outfit,' he added softly.

She coloured to the roots of her hair, but she stood her ground, forcing herself to ignore his sarcasm.

'Can we talk about that, please?' Sitting down opposite him, she poured some orange juice, and took a quick sip of hers. 'I know this sounds terribly...silly. And it's a cliché, too. But I don't know what came over me! If I gave an impression that...that I was interested in a...deeper relationship with you, I didn't intend to...'

'I apologised for that kiss, on the cliff,' Daniel cut in quietly. 'Do you want me to apologise for kissing you again in the study? If it'll make you feel better, I will. But if you want the truth I'm not sorry. To hell with convention. And to hell with not knowing who I am, and not knowing you too well either. I felt something for you the first time I saw you. When you came to the hospital, to ask how I was. I felt I knew you...'

'Daniel...'

'Let me finish.' He grinned bleakly. 'I thought you were someone who knew me, someone coming to tell me who I was.'

She stared at him, her breath catching in her throat.

'Did you?'

'That's why I was suspicious about this offer of accommodation,' he said coolly, reaching for the cheese roll and taking a bite.

'I'd never seen you before,' she assured him, slightly unsteadily. 'But when I saw you...at least...' She couldn't tell him she'd felt the same strange affinity, could she? Make an even bigger fool of herself?

'At least...what?'

'Nothing.' She drank some more juice, and picked up a cucumber stick, nibbling the end. 'I told you why I offered to help. I found you. Within just a few yards of my doorstep. It made sense to let you stay round here, help your memory to return...'

'And now we're fighting some strange compulsion to jump into bed with each other?' he finished up sardonically.

'That's not the way I'd describe it!'

'Probably not. But then you strike me as badly retarded when it comes to anything to do with sex.'

'That's not a very chivalrous thing to say.' How she kept from throwing the salad bowl at him she wasn't sure.

'It's OK, I won't push it,' he assured her calmly. 'Just don't float around in any more see-through blouses while I'm staying here.'

'Don't barge into my house unannounced again!' she snapped in a low voice. She was hot all over, rigid with mortification. 'Honestly, I've never met anyone like you! Even if this were a . . . a normal relationship, believe me, I'd never dream of jumping into bed with a man on two days' acquaintance!'

'Sometimes these things defy logic.'

'What a smug pronouncement!' She was really angry now. 'That's as bad as saying, This thing is bigger than both of us!'

He shrugged. 'This is good Cheddar,' he commented idly, finishing another bite of his roll. 'Mature, but not so strong it takes the back off your throat.'

She felt like strangling him.

'I'm glad it's to your taste! Listen, are you saying you think I'm some kind of . . . of nymphomaniac? Because if you are I . . .'

'Hey, cool down.' The green gaze was perceptive as he gazed at her flushed face. 'First, I don't think you're a nymphomaniac. Nymphomaniacs don't give off conflicting signals the way you do. They tend to go straight for the jugular...'

'You've met lots, then...'

'Stop switching track. We're talking about you. Second, I'm as confused about this attraction between us as you are...'

'Because I'm basically not the kind of woman who attracts men!' she summed up for him, bitterness escaping.

There was a silence.

'I told you.' He grinned at last, his eyes holding hers with a hypnotic kind of insistence. 'I'm probably from another planet. Maybe where I come from tall, shapely brunettes with Elizabeth Taylor eyes are all the rage.'

'Oh, go to hell...!' His taunting was unbearable. She stood up to go, and he said in a harder voice,

'Don't run away again.'

'I think it's better if we steer clear of each other from now on. You said you were happy to self-cater...'

'Carla, sit down.'

Frozen to the spot, she battled with that steely note in his voice. Resentfully, she did as he said.

'We need to talk this out,' he persisted quietly, 'and where's your sense of humour, for God's sake?'

'If you think it's funny, what happened just now in my study...'

The smile faded from his eyes. He reached to take her hand, pulled it between his, turned it over to look at the smooth softness of her palm.

'That wasn't funny at all. It was serious. The problem was, it came too fast, too soon. I'm fumbling in the dark here. The only thing I know for certain is that I find you...attractive.'

'But you hardly know me!' It was a painful whisper. 'And besides, I've never...'

'Never what?' he probed softly.

'Never...I've never felt like this before,' she finished up awkwardly. 'This...this physical thing...'

Daniel's glance was shuttered. 'Not even with...Rufus?'

'No.' Inside she was dying a dozen deaths. But the words seemed to be dragged from her. Something in the quality of Daniel's gaze, the way he was looking at her, gave her the courage she needed to risk it.

'So what do we do about it?' he murmured, twisting his lips into a lop-sided grin.

'I don't know...nothing.' She gave a shaky laugh, and tried to draw her hand away, but he held it between both of his.

'"Nothing" sounds like the wisest option. Besides, sex isn't all it's cracked up to be, is it?' He was teasing, she realised, almost fainting at the warm gleam of desire she saw in his eyes.

'Sex is a total waste of time,' she agreed shakily. 'Or at least it has been so far for me...'

He groaned under his breath. 'Don't make this more difficult for me, Carla. Don't put another layer of temptation in my path...'

'What do you mean?'

'Don't you know that no man can resist that kind of challenge? A woman claiming she doesn't enjoy sex?'

She stiffened. This time, she did snatch her hand away. He leaned back in his chair, and watched her.

'All this talk of sex,' she said at last, clutching at the shreds of her composure, 'as if it were the criterion for a good relationship! It's not. Without trust, mutual interests, respect, consideration...'

'Hold on——' he grinned again '—Miss Goody Two Shoes. Those things take time. We're talking about *lust* here, Carla. Plain, simple old lust. But don't knock it. I'm sure many a close relationship begins on lust alone.'

'Do you think being deliberately crude is clever?'

'And I should think more than a few relationships founder without it,' he added unrepentantly. 'The vibrations I get about your marriage make me suspect yours could be one of them.'

She stood up angrily, pale with humiliation.

'Thank you, Daniel. I was hoping something could...could break this *spell*, before I did something I'd regret. Now that I realise you're a crass, insensitive cynic, lust won't even get a look-in from now on...!'

Turning on her heel, she started to walk away. With unnerving speed, he was between her and the door, blocking her escape. The humour hadn't quite died from his eyes, but the cool, mocking expression she read there now made the breath disappear from her lungs. He wasn't touching her, but she was trapped in his eyes. It was like being caught in a magnetic force.

'"Lust" doesn't do justice to the way I'm feeling right now, Carla,' he murmured, with grim amusement. 'There must be a stronger word for it...'

With a stifled sound in her throat, she tried to rush past him. He caught her arm, twisting her round.

'Daniel...I...' Her croak of protest faded as he lifted his free hand to her face, then brushed the knuckles slowly along the curve of her cheek. Her heart had begun thumping fiercely.

'It's going to be hard for me to stay away from you, now I've glimpsed what you're hiding under that baggy disguise of yours.'

The deep voice was taunting, but there was a thicker trace of sexual desire. The raw male signals triggered a humiliating response deep inside her.

'Daniel, you said...you said you wouldn't push this...' She tried desperately to resist him, but every inch of her was reacting to everything about him, his nearness, his hooded, lazy gaze. The concentrated stillness in him. The touch of his fingers.

'I know I did. Maybe I've just changed my mind...' Without warning he jerked her closer, bent his head and kissed her.

His mouth was hard and warm, hungry on hers. Urgent beneath a thin layer of restraint. He drew back and raked a searching look over her flushed face.

'I'm only human, Carla. You're driving me crazy. One minute you're cold, the next you're hot...'

She knew she should fight, but instead some inner fire forced her to slide trembling arms round him. His muscled back was lean, and reassuringly strong beneath his shirt.

'Carla...!' The hoarse groan was ripped from him. With abrupt arrogance, he hauled her down on to the sofa, his hands sliding questingly beneath her jumper, seeking the vulnerable swell of her breasts.

'Oh...please...' It was a stifled sob, forced back into her throat as he deepened the kiss, forcing intimate possession of her mouth. The warm, persistent invasion of his tongue left her in no doubt of his desire to claim more. She shivered as he pushed up her jumper with masculine boldness, levered one muscled thigh between her jean-clad legs, thrust her back to explore her exposed body more thoroughly. She was on fire; she was burning up with feverish intensity. Like an emotional furnace roaring out of control...

'I want you, Carla...' Each breast was caressed and stroked, each peaked nipple was kissed in turn, then drawn deeper into the hardness of his mouth until she writhed and quivered, turning to jelly in his arms, her legs paralysed with the heavy inertia of desire... 'And you feel the same, don't you?' It wasn't really a question. It was a soft, confident assertion.

'I... yes... no... I feel... oh, I don't *know* how I feel...'

'Show me,' he suggested hoarsely, thickly, a glitter of hunger making his lidded eyes gleam like a lion's. 'Show me how you feel... I'm here, I'm on fire for you, Carla, and to hell with anything else; right now I'm all yours, sweetheart...'

His hands moved to the waistband of her jeans, his fingers thrusting lower, arousing a dark, secret throb of desire which shocked her in its intensity. She felt herself melting and heating inside. The dangerous hardness of his body through the rough Levis brought her to her senses, almost as much as the scorching bluntness of his words. If she let this go any further, if she let him touch her where he was going to touch her, she'd be lost... A shudder rocked through her as she searched for the strength to fight. To fight her way out of this sensual jungle he was spinning around her...

'No... *no!*' Her urgency communicated itself faster than she'd expected. He let her go, with an exaggerated lift of his hands which mocked her ruthlessly. She struggled furiously to her feet, leaving him sprawled lazily on the sofa. Dragging her jumper down, she glared at him, her knees infuriatingly weak and wobbly. What was she allowing to happen here? Just because surging hormones were flexing their strength! And he wasn't all hers! How could he say that, when he didn't even know *who* he was?

'No?' he mocked quietly, watching her with narrowed eyes. 'No. You're probably right. Too many complications.'

It didn't even merit a reply, she decided, a white-hot rage consuming her. She marched out shakily, and slammed the cottage door resoundingly behind her.

It was the following evening, the appointed hour for Becky's dinner invitation, before she spoke to Daniel again.

The rest of the previous afternoon had been spent tucked away in her study, pouring all her anger and frustration into her novel. Was it her imagination, or did the relationship between Jack Tresawna and Paula, his quiet, tawny-haired assistant, suddenly seem to be simmering with undercurrents of sexual tension? Reading over the print-outs, that night, in front of her fire, with a pizza and a glass of wine, she couldn't be sure. *Had* she written in more intimate conflict, or was it just her own besieged state of mind playing tricks?

The relationship between her two main protagonists had always been subtly ambiguous—something her readers seemed to enjoy. Two reserved, emotionally repressed individuals, working together

in their grim, harrowing profession, and sharing a
rapport which transcended the normal rules of
sexual desire or physical attraction.

She'd thought of Daniel with a fresh shiver of
anger. If a touch more physical awareness was
creeping into her novel, he was the culprit...

There'd been a lot of coming and going, while
she was writing. She'd been aware of it, but deliberately remained aloof. The doctor had visited
Daniel, as arranged, and spent about half an hour
in the cottage before driving off again. Then the
police had arrived, knocking on her door first to
explain that they were here to interview Daniel again
for any further clues. For a while, she'd found it
desperately hard not to dash across the yard to see
whether they'd uncovered Daniel's identity. But
pride had kept her glued to her chair. No doubt
he'd have the courtesy to let her know when his
memory did come back. She'd put the mental
blinkers on, immersing herself in her work, taking
no notice when the police car finally drove away.

Now, reluctantly getting ready for the evening at
Becky and Tom's, she felt a stab of conscience. She
realised that she'd been so stiff and proud, she'd
provided neither dinner last night nor breakfast and
lunch today. Worse still, while she'd been sulking
over here in the farmhouse, Daniel could have had
a dizzy spell, passed out, had some complication
from the surgery he'd undergone to correct the
haemorrhage after his fall...

Highly unlikely, she told herself, thinking of his raging display of machismo yesterday afternoon. But still . . . she steeled herself to check. Lifting the phone, she dialled the cottage number. It rang out, and rang out, with no answer. Panic shooting through her, she forgot the finishing touches to her appearance, thrust her stockinged feet into low-heeled black loafers, and dashed downstairs, across the courtyard, and into the cottage.

'Daniel . . . ?' Breathing hard, she nearly jumped out of her skin when he appeared from the direction of the bathroom, clad only in a low-slung green towel round his hips. He was still wet, water glistening on broad, muscular chest and strongly muscled arms and legs.

'Well, hello again,' he greeted her, mild amusement in his eyes. 'Is something wrong?'

'I tried to ring you,' she explained coolly, trying to keep her eyes from their mesmerised exploration of his body. 'There was no reply. I was afraid you might be ill . . .'

'Ill?'

'Felt dizzy, fallen . . .' she snapped impatiently. 'Do you have to query everything I say?'

He regarded her levelly, then slowly eyed her up and down.

'I'm fine. No cause for alarm. I was in the shower. I wouldn't have heard the telephone. Is that what you're wearing to dinner tonight?'

'Yes.' She held the green gaze for as long as she could, then dropped her eyes a little, feeling her cheeks warming. She'd been gripped by a contrary urge to deny her femininity as fiercely as she knew how. She'd dug into the back of her wardrobe and unearthed the most unflattering suit she possessed, one she'd worn when she was at least a stone heavier, in a murky shade of beige corduroy which did nothing for her colouring. With a muddy-brown polo neck, minimal make-up, and with her hair pushed back behind her ears, she knew she looked dowdy, plain, sexless and boring. Like someone's poor relation.

'Do you have a problem with it? If you do, you can always opt out of coming,' she added acidly. 'I'm sure Becky and Tom would understand!'

Shaking his head thoughtfully, he continued to examine her, then he turned back towards the bathroom.

'I guess not. If I do, I'll just visualise what's underneath.'

'Daniel . . . !'

The heat scalded her cheeks as she glared after his nonchalant figure. The lean muscles rippled in his shoulders, the long, powerful curve of calf and thigh-muscles hinted at an impressive level of fitness. Dragging her eyes away, she hugged her arms round herself, angrily defensive.

'Wait here, help yourself to a drink,' he called over his shoulder. 'I won't be long.'

She sat down on the chair by the fire. There was a tray of bottles and glasses on the table by the chimney breast. When had he been out shopping?

she wondered, deciding on a small, non-alcoholic ginger ale. She definitely hadn't provided whisky, gin, sherry and Martini. Was the man a dipsomaniac? Dashing to the shops to buy alcohol at the first opportunity? But the bottles were full. Presumably an alcoholic would have made a hefty hole in one of them by now...

She walked to the window, gazing across at the farmhouse, sipping her drink. She was already regretting dressing like this. It had been the only way she could think of to fight back against the escalating tension with Daniel. The only way she could think of to prove she wasn't scheming, vampishly, to ensnare him...

'Scotch looks a good idea. I'll join you.'

He'd appeared behind her soundlessly, and she spun round.

'I'm not drinking Scotch. This is ginger ale...' Her cool words faded as she stared at him in surprise. She'd expected to see him in denims and checked shirt again. Instead, he was wearing superbly tailored trousers, in plain dark green twill, with an oyster-coloured silk shirt and a black cashmere jumper. Round his shoulders was a butter-soft suede jacket, in a subtle shade of creamy tan. Immaculate brown leather brogues, and an elusive waft of some musky male aftershave completed the effect. The plaster had gone from his temple. Apart from the bruise, and the stitches, he looked tall, dark, and devastatingly handsome. The kind of cool, disturbing male who set female hearts fluttering with a single glance.

'What do you think?' he enquired calmly, pouring Scotch into his glass, taking a mouthful with a slight grimace of appreciation. 'I pawned the Rolex to raise some cash. One of my policeman friends drove me into Penzance.'

'You look ... very smart. But ...'

'Yes?'

'Well, that outfit looks so ... expensive,' she finished up doubtfully. 'How can you be sure you can afford clothes like that?'

'I can't. But I had to do something in honour of my dinner-date tonight,' he said lightly. 'I just followed my instincts. Plus, the value of the Rolex seemed to be enough to buy a couple of round-the-world cruises. So either I'm a rich villain, or whatever I do for a profession can stand me a set of decent clothes. Right down to a new supply of boxer-shorts. Are you ready? I'll have to beg a lift with you. I'm still car-less. I'd need a driving-licence to hire one.'

The cool, taunting tone in his voice confused, angered and hurt her at the same time. Tense and miserable, and feeling irrationally furious with her stubbornly ugly outfit, she nodded.

'Cheer up, Carla,' he advised, touching her cheek as she passed him at the door. 'Put a smile on your face at least. Your friends will think you're ill.'

'Maybe I feel ill,' she said shortly, driving through the narrow Cornish lanes towards Carperrow Farm.

'How are you feeling now? Are you up to socialising?'

'The headaches are getting better. But I doubt if I'm up to late partying.'

'I don't like late nights either. And Becky and Tom will be quite happy if we go early. Their baby has started waking them up in the middle of the night.'

'The perfect excuse for an early night, then,' he agreed, deadpan. His glance across at her made her pulses kick erratically.

'I'm *so* glad you could come,' Becky gushed a short time later, almost dragging them across the doorstep into the beamed cosiness of Carperrow Farm. 'Come on in, sit down, have a drink; what can I get you?'

'For heaven's sake, woman, let them catch their breath,' Tom said drily, shaking hands with Daniel and kissing Carla on the cheek.

There was a cheerful log fire, Enya playing softly on the hi-fi.

'Are you all right, Carla?' Becky was frowning at her in concern. 'You look awfully pale, love.'

'I'm fine.'

'I haven't seen you wear that outfit for... ages,' her friend added, a disapproving note in her voice. 'Heavens, you remind me of someone...'

'Me too. I've just thought who it is,' Daniel murmured in Carla's ear, with a wicked smile. 'Julie Andrews, fresh from the abbey in the dress the poor didn't want.'

'I know it's a bit dated,' Carla agreed stiffly, flashing Daniel a baleful glance. 'I was just in a rush to get ready. I was writing all afternoon; I didn't notice the time...'

'Don't apologise, darling,' Becky assured her, with a laugh. 'Actually you might start a trend!'

'Yeah, charity-shop rejects for the discerning frump,' Daniel teased under his breath.

Carla had never felt so wound up towards violence. Clenching her fists behind her, she had to make a mammoth effort to smile and act normally for Becky's watchful eyes.

Tom began talking to Daniel about the accident, his amnesia, demanding progress reports. Becky, on the pretext of taking Carla to see the baby up in the nursery, drew her out of earshot.

'What's going on?' she demanded, half laughing, when they reached the landing outside Flora's pretty yellow and white room. 'I've seen you make more effort with your appearance when you're *gardening*!'

'I've always been a frump, remember?' Carla countered, unable to hide her surge of bitterness. 'My late husband told me so, every other day of our marriage...'

'Carla, that's total rubbish!' Becky's voice sharpened. 'You're absolutely stunning, and you know it. But even the most beautiful woman can make herself look a mess if she deliberately tries!'

Carla met her friend's eyes with a faint, rueful smile.

'Is it that obvious?'

'It is to me! So what's the story?'

'Don't ask,' Carla advised bleakly. 'Let's just say I'm taking the line of least provocation. I'm trying to avoid making a total fool of myself...'

'With Daniel?'

Colour crept into her face as she met Becky's curious brown eyes. 'With Daniel,' she confirmed huskily. 'The ridiculous thing is, Becky...' She swallowed on a thickened, constricted throat, and tried to laugh off the tension without success. 'The unbelievable thing is... I might be falling in love with him...'

CHAPTER FIVE

'DID you enjoy the evening?'

Daniel's query was expressionless as Carla drew the car up outside the house, and cut the engine. He'd been very cool since they'd said their goodbyes and left to come home.

'I always enjoy Becky and Tom's company,' she said carefully, avoiding his eyes. 'How about you? I suppose at least it was nice to get out and make contact with the real world again?'

'As opposed to lying in hospital beds or just conversing with you?'

'Quite.' His tone was ironic, but she felt unsure whether there'd been a trace of truth beneath the mockery. 'I hope you didn't feel too much the outsider,' she added stiffly, 'with the three of us indulging in village gossip all night?'

'I felt very welcome. I like your friends.' Daniel shot her a shrewd glance, adding, 'I got the impression they're very protective of you.'

She stiffened, reaching for the door-handle but not opening the door.

'Protective?' She glanced at Daniel suspiciously. He was so . . . perceptive. For a while tonight, after Becky's excellent *coq au vin* and lemon soufflé, the four of them had looked at old photographs. She couldn't remember why Becky had produced them, but there had been some showing herself and Rufus together, with Becky and Tom, on an Easter weekend break, a couple of years ago.

Daniel had inspected one photograph with such poker-faced concentration, she'd felt compelled to look over his shoulder to see. It had been herself and Rufus, sitting in a tapas bar at Ocean Village, in Southampton, in the pale April sun. They hadn't looked like a loving husband and wife, exactly. But they'd been laughing at the camera. Rufus's hair, that brilliant shock of red-gold, had gleamed in the sunlight. Had Tom or Becky said something to Daniel, while she'd popped upstairs to the loo, perhaps? Something personal, about the disastrous failure of her marriage?

'Protective in what way?' she persisted.

'As if they've seen you hurt, and they're determined not to see it happen again.' Was there a new edge to his voice? Some inexplicable trace of damped-down emotion?

'You're imagining things,' she said shortly. 'Frankly, Daniel, you're altogether too inquisitive about other people!'

'Maybe I'm a student of human nature?' The hard mouth twisted in self-mockery.

Decisively, Carla snatched the door-handle and got out, slamming the door behind her. Daniel followed more calmly, and faced her across the roof of the car.

'If I'm too inquisitive, you're too defensive,' he asserted, coming round to stand beside her, looking down into her pale face. 'Maybe I make my living out of being inquisitive . . . ?'

'Maybe you do,' she agreed icily. 'A market researcher, perhaps? No, you're probably a tax inspector.'

He grimaced. 'God help me,' he murmured wryly. 'Or one of those Customs officials who strip-search people for drugs?'

His flippant grin caught at her self-control. She started to laugh, in spite of herself, and then the laughter died.

'I don't know how you can be so . . . nonchalant about it,' she said shakily. 'If I had no idea who I was, where I'd come from, I'd be a mental wreck . . .'

Daniel's smile was enigmatic. But his eyes held a touch of grimness. There was a fraction of a pause, before he said quietly, 'So I'm a nonchalant mental wreck.'

She stared up at him, her heart suddenly thudding.

'I really enjoyed tonight,' she said impulsively. 'I feel as if we've known each other for ages . . .' Becky and Tom must have felt the same, she knew. The rapport between them all had been high, Daniel's contribution to the evening drily witty, sharply observant and surprisingly intellectual, philosophical. At one stage, she recalled him touching on the complex theories of Pythagoras as if sixth-century-B.C. Greek philosophers were as

familiar to him as the alphabet. And he'd even
made the subject sound funny. He was a fascinating, intriguing, infuriating enigma. And a total
stranger, she reminded herself brutally. She mustn't
forget that...

The pause stretched out unbearably.

'Do... do you want some coffee?'

'Thanks...' He lifted his hand to touch her cheek
briefly with his finger, then stepped away. There
was a guarded expression in his eyes, an expression
she hadn't seen before. 'I think I'll take a rain-check
on that. Goodnight, Carla...'

He bent to kiss her cheek lightly, and she caught
her breath involuntarily. The small, choked sound
in her throat made him stop, and look into her up-
turned face. She couldn't speak. Her lower lip
tightly gripped in her teeth, she met his eyes. She
felt as if everything stopped. They were frozen in
time. The moon was silvering everything, ghostly-
bright. The moment seemed to vibrate. Her heart
seemed to swell in her chest.

She desperately wanted him to kiss her, she
realised, with a blinding flash of enlightenment. She
wanted to feel his lips on hers, that warm spiral of
bliss he could create right through the centre of her
whole body, just by covering her mouth with his,
and sliding his thumbs possessively along her
jawline, and over the sensitive flesh just behind her
ears...

'Daniel...' Her voice was barely audible, a husky,
half-ashamed invitation.

'Goodnight, Carla.'

Coolly, he swung on his heel and walked across the yard, disappearing into the cottage without a backward glance. Shakily, slowly, she locked the car, and went in to bed. She didn't put on any lights. She felt too shell-shocked by her emotions. It was what she'd wanted, wasn't it? A way of retreating from a situation that was fast getting out of control. A crazy situation which could never come to anything, never work . . .

She didn't want to see herself clearly in the mirror, remind herself cruelly what a complete fright she looked. The moon was so brilliant, she could see all she wanted to see as she dropped her clothes on a chair, stood beneath a soothing warm shower, then huddled into bed. She expected to lie awake for hours, curled miserably into a ball under the duvet, but she fell almost instantly asleep.

She wasn't sure at first what woke her. Stirring in the warmth of the covers, she blinked into the darkness. Was it the wind and the rain that had woken her? The clear moonlit night of a few hours ago had degenerated into a storm. The rain was lashing torrentially in from the ocean, flinging itself against her window like handfuls of pebbles.

But no, it wasn't the rain. She identified the sound she'd heard. Tyres on wet gravel. The muffled clunk of a car door, down in the courtyard. Slipping out of bed, she stumbled to the window overlooking the yard, and stared blankly down at the scene below. A sea mist had come in with the bad weather. Through the foggy wetness, there was a police car, parked near the cottage. Lights glowed from the cottage sitting-room, through a chink in the heavy red velvet curtains.

Bewildered, half asleep, she racked her brains as she tried to work out what was going on. The police, here again, in the middle of the night? In this weather? Was Daniel in some sort of trouble? Had they suddenly uncovered evidence about his identity? Carla frowned, rubbing her eyes. He'd said something about a policeman 'friend', earlier. The man who'd driven him into Penzance, to pawn his Rolex. But even so... what was he doing back here in the early hours of the morning?

She looked dubiously at the telephone. Dared she ring? Reveal that she'd been spying out of her bedroom window? She pulled a face to herself in the dark. It wasn't spying, exactly, was it? She hadn't asked to be woken up in the middle of the night by a police car, had she?

Hesitating, she wavered for a few more minutes. Then curiosity and a degree of alarm got the better of her. If Daniel was about to frog-marched away in handcuffs, she definitely wanted to speak to him first...

The number rang, and rang. Just the way it had earlier that evening. Baffled, she waited until it was quite clear nobody was going to answer. She hung up and tried again. And again. Still nothing. A noise outside in the courtyard made her jerk around, and drop the telephone receiver back on its cradle. She ran to the window. The policeman had got back in the car, was reversing, driving away, headlights refracted in the mist and rain, wipers swishing sheets of rain off the windscreen. Was Daniel in the car with him? It was too wet and dark to see. A wave of apprehension, concern and then pure fear combined to trigger total panic.

Unthinking, she grabbed her white satin robe, and raced downstairs, out of the house, and into the wildness of the night. The wind took her breath away. Almost instantly, in the thin blue satin of her pyjamas, even with the robe, she felt soaked to the skin. She'd forgotten shoes or slippers. The gravel hurt her feet. Something caught her toe as she ran through the stormy darkness, and she tripped and fell with a cry of angry impatience. Stumbling back to her feet, she limped the short distance remaining and made it to the cottage, and stood shivering and soaked to hammer furiously on the door.

It could only have been a couple of minutes before the door opened, but it felt like a couple of hours. When it did finally open, and Daniel stood there, she almost sobbed with relief.

'You *are* still here!' she gasped idiotically, almost falling inside. 'I thought you'd been arrested or something . . . !'

He drew her inside, and slammed the door against the rain. Then he looked her over with an expression of combined disbelief and amusement.

'I'd say you're the one who needs locking up,'

he said flatly, leading her towards the fire. Miraculously, it was still smouldering. Had he been sitting up all night? But he was dressed for bed. At least, undressed for bed. All he seemed to be wearing was a navy velvet-towelling robe, belted, calf-length. The piratical growth of stubble on his jaw gave him a tough, disturbing air. 'What in hell's name are you doing running barefoot in the rain, wearing only this flimsy thing?'

She stiffened as he pushed her down on the chair, and threw another log on to the fire.

'I was worried about you,' she ground out furiously, with a shiver. 'But now that I'm here I can't think why! You're such an ungrateful slob, I wish I'd just gone back to bed and let you rot!'

Daniel was pouring her a glass of Scotch, handing it to her with an unreadable look.

'Let me rot?' he echoed.

'The *police* car woke me,' she explained stiffly. 'I tried to ring you to find out if everything was all right. You didn't answer, so I came to see . . .'

'Barefoot?' he confirmed, tilting an eyebrow. 'In the rain?'

'Daniel, I thought you might have been *arrested*!'

'Right. I understand. You've suspected all along that I'm an escaped convict.'

'Oh, for heaven's sake . . . !' She took a drink of the Scotch, and felt the warmth glow down her throat. 'If you're not going to tell me what's going on, that's up to you!'

'First, the telephone is out of order,' he said quietly, eyeing her soaked and shivering state with a grim set to his jaw. 'It rings at the caller's end, but not here. Remember you tried to ring me earlier this evening?'

She nodded slowly. 'Is that why the police called in person? They'd tried to ring you?'

'That's it. They were concerned, like you, when they got no reply.'

'But they could have rung me.'

Daniel's eyes were shuttered as he shrugged.

'Slightly antisocial in the middle of the night. It was me they needed to talk to... Carla, you'd better let me look at your foot. You're bleeding all over the carpet.'

Shocked, she jerked her head down. Although her foot was so cold she felt nothing, she'd obviously cut it when she tripped. Trembling slightly, she handed him back the glass.

'I'd better go back to the farmhouse,' she began shakily; 'I've got some plasters there...'

'I've some here,' he cut in calmly. 'Hospital issue. I'm supposed to be wearing one on these stitches all the time.' He gestured briefly to the healing wound on his temple. 'And you're not going anywhere, Carla. Apart from into a hot bath...'

'Don't be silly, there's absolutely no need...' she began, horrified, then squeaked involuntarily as she put weight on her foot and tried to stand up. With a short laugh, Daniel bent and lifted her easily into his arms.

'Come along,' he teased. 'Uncle Daniel to the rescue . . .'

Being carried by Daniel was an experience Carla had to close her eyes to endure.

She felt she should wriggle in protest, but she kept quite still. First, because she had a nagging fear that he shouldn't be carrying eight and a half stone of female around, in his condition. And second, because the sensation of his hard chest, warm against her breasts, was so overwhelming that she felt frozen in shame. How could she have become so . . . sensually aware?

'Daniel, this *is* ridiculous,' she tried at last, in a muffled voice against his shoulder. 'I've only scratched my foot, and got wet in the rain . . . !'

Ignoring her, he sat her on the padded stool by the bath, and twisted on the taps.

'You'd be wise to get a tetanus injection tomorrow,' he commented briefly, as the welcoming steam began to fill the bathroom. 'Which of these bath-foams do you prefer?' He picked up the bottles she'd left on the ledge for her various lodgers, and waved them at her. 'Damask rose or jojoba?'

'That one.' She pointed jerkily at the creamy bottle of jojoba, and glared at him, suppressing a shiver as the soaked satin of her pyjamas and robe cooled against her skin. 'And all this fussing over me is cleverly evading the point, isn't it? *What* did the police have to talk to you about so urgently?'

'Get in the bath; we'll talk when you're warm and dry,' he said firmly.

As she stared at him, the colour crept into her cheeks. 'I hope you're not suggesting I put on a bathtime show for your benefit?' she snapped. Her knowledge of her own dismal vulnerability made her even angrier.

'Only if you want to.'

Her colour deepened, and she began to stand up, her eyes blazing.

'OK, I get the message,' he teased wickedly, backing out of the room. 'I'll see you later . . . Wait a minute.' He left the room briefly and returned with a brand-new pair of navy blue silk pyjamas, still unwrapped. 'Wear these when you're ready,' he added, closing the door firmly behind him as he went out.

Looking around her in helpless fury, she could see very little option. She stripped off the wet things, eased herself into the hot bath, and shuddered with reluctant pleasure. The contrast of her chilled limbs with the steamy, fragrant bath was too hedonistic to ignore.

The cut on her foot wasn't as deep as she'd thought. But her toe was sore, where she'd crashed into the offending object in the dark. Soaking blissfully in the warmth, everything seemed to get better—the pain in her foot, the shivering in her body, the suppressed anger knotting her up inside. By the time she stepped out and dried herself, and pulled on the new silk pyjamas, she'd begun to see the funny side.

The navy pyjamas were enormous on her. She had to roll up the legs, roll up the sleeves. Towelling her hair, she gave herself a cursory glance in the mirror before braving Daniel's opinion down in the sitting-room.

'Better?' he enquired calmly. He was sitting by the fire, a small whisky in one hand, her copy of *The Moon's Men* in the other. She'd firmly resolved to tackle him again on the mysterious police visit, when she spotted Moppy, stretched out in front of the fire. The cat was lying on his back, in one of his silliest positions, paws in the air, with an expanse of fluffy pale-cream under-fur exposed, calmly drying himself in the warmth. He made an exotic contrast against the richly textured red and gold hearthrug.

She limped towards him, seeking the warmth of the fire.

'Yes, better. I see Moppy's adopted you. I hope you don't mind cats...'

'No, I like cats. This one's quite a character. He was mewing at the door...'

She sat down on the sofa opposite Daniel, and reached out a bare toe to tickle Moppy's tummy, then retracted it quickly before he could decide to retaliate with his claws.

'Well...this is the second time I've panicked about you because I couldn't get an answer on the phone,' she said, with a small laugh. 'But from now on I get the message. Physically, even after that crack on the head, you're probably fitter than I am. You're perfectly able to look after yourself...'

Daniel's closeness made her nervous all over again. She waited a few seconds for him to say something, offer some explanation about the mysterious police visit. He said nothing. She heard herself gabbling on.

'I think there's an umbrella somewhere in the hall, and there must be an old pair of wellies I leave for guests to use. I'll make a run for it...'

'Let me have a look at your foot.' A trace of hoarseness in his voice made her glance at him.

She didn't move. Suddenly, her heart had begun to thump, almost audibly. He got up, and crouched down in front of her, lifting the injured foot to inspect it. Her toes were still pink from the warm bath, the underside of her foot very soft as he clasped it in his hand. Her heartbeat was now a dull booming sound in her ears. The feel of his fingers on her foot, strong and firm, and somehow subtly sensual even without moving, was firing a kind of anger inside her. No, not anger. Warmth. Fire. A hungry flame of need. She was trembling again, she realised distantly.

'Daniel...' Her voice was just a whisper.

'Carla, sweetheart, if you keep looking at me like that, I'm not going to be able to stop myself from making love to you right now...'

'I don't know how I'm looking at you. Don't blame me. It's the way you're touching my foot...'

'How am I touching your foot?' The huskiness in his voice had intensified. His green gaze had darkened abruptly. Become almost opaque with desire. His hand moved, a slow caress, around her bare ankle and up towards the slender muscle of her calf. What was wrong with her? she wondered dumbly as she stared into his eyes. She shivered convulsively.

'Daniel . . .' It was a muffled sob, torn from her in spite of her reservations. 'Oh, Daniel . . .'

With a soft groan, he lowered his head and dropped a kiss on her little toe. She caught her breath, a sharp sound which made him look up at her. Their eyes locked, he kissed the ankle-bone, then turned her foot gently over to run his lips hungrily over the softness of the instep. She was rigid, melting inside, her whole body alive with sensation.

'You have the most delicate feet I've ever seen,' he murmured thickly. The warm, hungry exploration of his mouth moved higher. Closing her eyes, flung into a kind of trance, she let her senses drift and swim in the tide of desire washing over her. The navy pyjamas were loose. The material pushed easily away to expose her leg up to the knee, and with each devouring movement of his mouth the shivers of reaction intensified.

She was shuddering convulsively by the time he reached to click off the table-lamp and pull her decisively down to the hearthrug, holding her so closely in his arms she could smell the clean freshness of his skin, inside the towelling robe. His hardness and strength made her senses swim.

With a disdainful mew, Moppy jumped to his feet and retreated to the sofa, turning his back on them.

In the flickering firelight, Daniel slowly unbuttoned the navy silk top, drew the fastening open to expose her breasts to his view.

'You're trembling like a leaf,' he pointed out hoarsely, inspecting the arch of her throat, the symphony of hollows and curves, with darkened, lidded eyes. 'Are you frightened of me, Carla?'

'No... not frightened...' She sought to explain how she felt, but her throat was too choked with emotion. 'I'm no good at this,' she finished up with a choked laugh, tensing as his hands smoothed the swell of her breasts, cupped the fullness, his thumbs rotating over the tight peaks of her nipples.

'No good?' he chided with a devastating smile. 'Believe me, you're good. You're good enough to eat, sweetheart, all over...'

'Oh...!' It was a gasp of suppressed reaction, part fear, part joy. Instinctively, she reached up her arms, let her fingers rake into his dark hair, slipped her hands down the lean hardness of his back, and closed her eyes.

It was like a dream, she reflected hazily. A dream which was real. The kind of dream which seemed so real when you woke, it made real life seem a lie. There was no music playing, no softly sensual guitar-chords or Vangelis's pulsating 'Chariots of

Fire', but there should have been. Because the way Daniel was making her feel, the shivery ecstasy he was awakening, was the kind of subtle surge of emotion she'd only ever felt before while listening to her favourite music.

Slowly, inexorably, while the thick, carnal silence wrapped itself around them, she let herself be transported to another dimension.

'Carla, sweetheart...' The deep, possessive caress in his voice made her open her eyes. Dazzled, she gazed up at him. The smile she provoked held triumph, hunger, and a question. 'This may not be a good idea...'

'Oh...please...' she whispered shakily, twisting beneath his seeking hands, beside herself in the heights of arousal. 'It is...'

The blue silk pyjama trousers were no obstacle to the ultimate intimacy. With a softly muttered curse, Daniel stripped her last covering away, discarded the towelling robe, and pinned her beneath him while he searched her flushed face for answers.

'I want you,' he groaned. His eyes moved intently over her slender body, the high, full thrust of her breasts, the curve of waist and hips, the long, sculpted line of thighs and calves spread out beneath him, like a starving man viewing a feast.

'You're beautiful, my shy little Carla. I want to lose myself inside you, sweetheart...'

'Daniel...' She breathed his name with soft passion. 'It's all right; love me, make love to me, it's what I want...'

'Don't regret this too much, sweetheart,' he muttered, her husky words tripping the wire of his control. He crushed her powerfully into his arms, forcing a place for himself between her trembling knees, yet still retaining sufficient leash on his desire to probe gently for access, before he drove deeply, and irretrievably, to take what she offered.

She cried out huskily. The cry was muffled by his mouth as he thrust his tongue against hers in hungry unison with the fierce lunge of male possession. Carla clung to him, as she would to a lifebelt in a storm. Every preconceived notion of how it might be, how it should be, crumbled to dust as the reality surpassed each one of them. The feelings whirling through her were indescribable. Elation, frenzy, euphoria...

'Oh, yes, sweetheart...' Daniel had raised himself to look down at her flushed, shining face, his own carved with triumphant lines, the conqueror surveying his spoils. 'Give it all, Carla, let it go, just that way, sweetheart, exactly that way...'

'Daniel... oh, Daniel, I...' The abrupt eruption of inner spasms caught her by surprise, her mouth in a soft 'O' of shocked delight. Through a red mist, she could hear a voice moaning huskily, a rising, repetitive, out of control gasping, incoherent with pleasure, and realised it was her own voice.

With a rough laugh, he crushed her beneath him, the fierce, triumphant, shuddering pulse of his own climax ripping through him, ricocheting through both of them.

Afterwards, she lay in dreamy exhaustion, her arms wrapped round his hard body, while the carriage clock ticked ponderously on the shelf above the ingle-nook fireplace.

'Well?' he murmured at last, lifting his head to smile teasingly into her dazed face. 'How was it for you?'

She laughed softly at the wry humour. She loved his sense of humour. In fact, she loved *him*, she realised, half despairingly, half excitedly...she loved him. She loved this man, whoever he was, whatever he was... He was the first, the only man she'd *ever* loved... The knowledge surged through her, a violent elation, heady as champagne bubbles, almost as intense as the sexual fulfilment she'd just experienced through Daniel's expert, devastating lovemaking...

'The earth moved,' she whispered solemnly, her eyes dancing.

'It did?'

'Definitely.'

'Funny,' he murmured, kissing her ear. 'I thought it did too.'

'You never did put that plaster on my foot,' she reminded him huskily, smiling up into his dark face.

'No, I didn't. I hope you haven't bled all over the rug...'

'I don't think I have.' The colour surged into her face, and he laughed at her sudden embarrassment.

'Here, put my pyjamas on again,' he ordered. 'You'll get cold.' He reached for his robe, shrugging it on as he went in search of the plasters. Returning to the fireside, he tenderly lifted her foot, kissed it again lingeringly, then inspected the cut.

'No blood at all,' he confirmed softly, applying the sticking-plaster, and smoothing it deftly in place. 'You'll live, as my mother used to say...'

There was a sudden silence. The log hissed gently on the fire. Carla stared at him in abrupt confusion. The impact of his words, the reason for her confusion, took a few seconds to sink in. Then she froze, staring at him intently.

'Your mother?' she said quietly.

Daniel's mouth twisted wryly, but his eyes were steady.

'Yup. My mother used to say, "You're a wounded little soldier, but you'll live."'

The next silence was so deep, the tick of the old carriage clock on the ledge was almost deafening.

'You've remembered,' she said in a low, bewildered voice. But her senses were splintering.

Daniel's face was unreadable. But his gaze never left hers.

'Well? Aren't you going to say anything? Tell me what you've remembered?' she demanded shakily. Some secret part of her, buried inside, shrank from knowing. She realised she didn't want reality to intrude on this cocoon of intimacy, this suspended moment in time. 'Daniel? Who are you?'

'Do you really want to know?' His voice was quieter, tinged with a wry kind of irony which made her tense apprehensively.

'*Yes!*' she whispered desperately. 'Just tell me...?'

He shrugged, briefly, with an odd gesture of defeat.

'Remember you mentioned the back-stabbing friend who'd ruined your husband's career prospects?' he said flatly, expressionlessly. 'That's me, Carla. I'm Leo Tremayne...'

CHAPTER SIX

CARLA found herself wondering if this was a dream. Or rather, a nightmare. In a moment, she'd wake up in her own bed and mull it all over in a befuddled way, then go back to sleep...

'Well?' Daniel prompted softly, when the silence had deepened for several minutes. 'Am I going to get any verbal reaction, Carla? Or do you plan to sit there all night, staring at me as if I were a ghost?'

'I...would I know? If you were or not?' she whispered at last, bitterness in her smile. 'Right now, I think I'd believe anything possible...'

'Even if I were dead, which I'm not——' he grinned bleakly '—why should the ghost of Leo Tremayne come and haunt you?'

'Because in a way he's already haunted me,' she said slowly. 'All through my marriage there was the spectre of Leo Tremayne. According to Rufus, his old schoolfriend Leo Tremayne was the most selfish, arrogant, egotistical bastard he'd ever had the misfortune to know...!'

And the most exciting, daring, fascinating man Carla had ever heard of, she reminded herself silently. Rufus's embittered tales of Leo Tremayne's exploits had sunk deep into her psyche, she realised with a jolt of dim recognition.

A war was being fiercely waged, inside her head and her heart . . .

'Quite an impressive epitaph, if I were a ghost,' Daniel murmured. The light, mocking tone masked a harder trace in his voice. He was withdrawing, mentally. Just as he was withdrawing physically, moving back off the floor beside her to sit on the chair. There was a cautious air of containment about him now.

Scrambling up off the floor herself, she retreated to the kilim-covered sofa, her eyes searching his face. She found little to reassure her in the dark, mask-like features. Clutching her arms around herself, she felt abruptly frightened, and vulnerable. And threatened . . . threatened in a way she didn't understand. There was an ache inside her, opening up like a black well. She'd just given herself to this man as if she'd trusted him with her own life . . . For the first time ever, she'd felt driven to open up totally. To give everything, physically, emotionally. And she'd been tricked. He'd known who he was, and kept it secret. He'd taken advantage of her silly, starry-eyed infatuation tonight, knowing that when she learned who he really was she'd be devastated . . .

Who he really was . . . Fragments of the past slipped back into her mind. Rufus, white-faced and bitter, spilling vitriol over yet another bottle of wine, or whisky, or gin, or whatever he could lay his hands on, his misery triggered by Leo, his oldest schoolfriend, who had double-crossed him, set him up, done him out of nearly all his invested money, and ultimately sacked him...

Leo Tremayne, she recalled Rufus telling her, had gone into the business straight from school. It had been run by a friend of Leo's father, who'd been something to do with Intelligence, in the army. When Rufus had joined them, after his spell at Sandhurst, he'd got on well with the older man. But relations with Leo had deteriorated. Jealousy, Rufus had scornfully maintained. Leo hadn't fancied army life. Having a father in the army had maybe turned him against the idea. Besides, someone as wayward and 'bolshie' as Leo wouldn't have lasted five minutes in the strict army discipline...

When Rufus had joined the company, the ex-army man had appreciated the Sandhurst training, treated Rufus with the respect he deserved. But Leo had done nothing but pick fault, criticise Rufus for his lifestyle and habits. Then the business had begun to lose money. Badly. When the older partner had retired, there'd been the chance to buy out his shares, but Rufus hadn't wanted to throw any more good money after bad. Leo had bought the older man's entire share, then, because Rufus had been desperate for money, he'd agreed to buy out Rufus too. He'd become the boss. Rufus had stayed on in his employ, bitterly regretting his decision, and his lack of capital...but even when the business had begun to pick up again, and begun to do really well, Leo had still seemed too determined to display ruthless power over Rufus. Out of the blue, just when things were going well, he'd sacked him...

'I don't understand. If you're Leo Tremayne, who is Daniel?' she managed, in a choked, cold voice.

'Me.' He watched the frown deepen on her forehead, and shrugged briefly. His expression was unreadable. 'My name is Daniel. Daniel Tremayne. Leo is a nickname. One dating back to public-school days. Which is why Rufus always called me Leo. Just like I always knew Rufus as Red...'

'Leo?' she demanded impatiently. 'A nickname for *Daniel*?'

Daniel quirked a fleeting smile at her disbelief. 'Daniel in the lion's den. Leo, as in lion. I was a bit headstrong. I played some schoolboy pranks which everyone decided were daring. You can probably imagine the kind of thing.'

She stared at him, absorbing this. Daring? Headstrong? She didn't know him well enough to judge. Realising that, she felt even angrier. But, on evidence to date, she supposed he didn't appear to lack the more mature versions of those dubious qualities. He didn't seem to lack courage or initiative... She thought of Rufus's resentful stories. Yes, she reflected despairingly. She *could* imagine exactly the kind of thing...

A shiver ran down her spine. What kind of bizarre coincidence had brought Leo Tremayne here? Maybe it was just too much to take in at this

time of night, but her head was spinning. She felt
slightly sick with tension and shock . . .

'So . . . the business you and Rufus were *briefly*
involved in together?' She forced herself to go on,
trying to control the shivering. 'The . . . the private
detective agency? Is that what you're still doing?
That's what you are? A private detective?'

Daniel nodded slowly. 'It wasn't that brief a
partnership, Carla. Rufus and I operated together
for nearly four years . . .'

'Until you forced him out?'

Daniel regarded her levelly. The sea-green gaze
was very clear, intent on her face. In spite of her
anguish, she felt her heart contract.

'Red and I had a lot of disagreements. I bought
out the senior partner and then I bought out Rufus.
Now I own and run Tremayne International——'

'Having walked all over Rufus to achieve it?'

Daniel ignored the barbed interruption.

'The company has grown a lot since Red was involved. I have offices in America and Europe . . .'

'You mean you have employees in grubby raincoats spying on people all over the world?'

The bitter sarcasm drew no anger. The green gaze
was steady.

'My employees rarely wear grubby raincoats,' he
said calmly, 'unless an undercover assignment
specifically calls for one, that is. We specialise in
general fraud, serious crime, and international
counterfeit investigation.'

'Should I be impressed?'

'Yeah, why not?' Daniel's wary coolness broke for a few seconds. The teasing smile flashed again, attacking her defences. 'We do a good job. Counterfeit is probably the biggest threat to legitimate world trade. We investigate anything from fake designer clothes and jewellery to fake fungicides which could destroy a country's entire crop, to counterfeit drugs which could poison the people they're intended to cure. I'd say you should be impressed.'

'In fact, you're Superman, saving the world?'

Conflicting emotions felt like a tornado, whirling round inside her. Daniel noticed her shivering. He said something under his breath, and stood up, taking a step towards her.

'Please,' she said tautly, 'don't touch me.'

'Carla, you're shaking,' he said quietly. 'For God's sake, come here...'

She resisted the firm grip on her wrist until the pressure became too strong. She was jerked, rigid as a board, into the warm hardness of Daniel's arms.

'Miss Prinn at the village post office said you were probably a rapist on the prowl,' Carla whispered fiercely, battling with her own responses. 'It just goes to show. Never trust a stranger...'

'I've been perfectly trustworthy,' Daniel countered gruffly against the top of her head, 'under provocation...'

'Provocation?' Her angry echo was muffled.

'I rate wandering around in black see-through blouses, and wet satin pyjamas, as extreme provocation . . .'

'Daniel . . . !'

'Not even tonight's antidote could undo the damage done.'

She fought free, pushing him away, and glaring up at him.

'What are you talking about?' she bit out.

'The orphanage-reject outfit?' The cool taunt in his eyes was unbearable. How could he be so flippant?

'This is all one big *joke* to you,' she whispered, the truth dawning. 'You just saw me as . . . as an object, a source of passing entertainment . . .'

'You've certainly been entertaining,' he agreed calmly.

Stiffening in fresh outrage, she balled her fists. She stared at him in mounting disbelief. The green eyes were slightly narrowed, but cool, expressionless. The hard features were unreadable.

'I'll make some tea,' he said with a slight shrug. 'You look to me as if you're in mild shock.'

Without waiting for a retort, he turned and disappeared into the kitchen. There were sounds of the kettle being filled, the chink of cups on a tray. Feeling numb, she subsided on to the sofa again, and curled her legs up beside her, staring at the fire. She loved open fires. If you lived alone, they were like having a friend in the room with you. The flames danced and flickered, licked round the outer bark of one of the apple logs. A steady hissing noise began as the heat penetrated the wood and the sap started to ooze. Outside, the wind and rain continued unabated. In here, in the shadows of the cottage sitting-room, with only the firelight, it was cosy and warm. But she felt detached, almost disorientated...

He came back with two steaming mugs of tea, and clicked on the table-lamp. The look he gave her as he handed her a mug was warily quizzical.

'Feeling any better?'

'Don't talk to me as if I were a sick child!' she said, in a low voice. She curled her fingers round the heat of the mug, and took a slow sip. It was strong, slightly sweetened. She made an impatient face.

'And I don't take sugar in my tea! For goodness' sake, I am *not* in shock!'

'You're not standing where I am,' he countered easily, surveying her huddled shape with an air of practised expertise. 'There's no colour in your face. And you're still trembling. Look at your hands.'

'Don't flatter yourself,' she retorted. 'If you think your sexual technique packs that much punch, your ego's even bigger than I thought!'

'I thought I did a pretty good job.' He grinned, with a taunting glint in his eyes.

'You would!' She fought the flood of heat to her cheeks, without success, and her embarrassment made her even angrier. 'You're just the type to gloat and brag. I can imagine you... *boasting* about your conquests! I can see now that everything Rufus said about you was true!'

'Is there any point in denying it?'

'No, because you can't!'

'Then I won't waste the energy. I've been a mythical villain in your life for too long, haven't I? Why try to shoot down years of folklore?'

'You're detestable,' she managed. She was so angry, she felt as if her blood was about to boil in her veins.

'Quite. A "crass, insensitive cynic",' he agreed. 'And that was the verdict before you knew I was Public Enemy Number One.'

'My judgement wasn't so bad after all!'

He made a wry face. 'The irony is that, purely by chance, I ended up here.'

'So where *were* you heading?'

'Here.'

Blankly, she stared at him. Now she was really bewildered. What was he talking about?

'Daniel, you're not making sense...'

'I was coming to see you.' He shrugged, putting his tea down on the table and sitting opposite her, his eyes bleakly amused. 'I'd just finished an undercover assignment. I still do a few hand-picked ones, though my cover's pretty well blown these days. The last bit brought me down as far as Plymouth. I'd only recently heard about Red's death. And, although we parted on bad terms, he and I went back a long way. To prep-school days, in fact. I had an urge to come and check up on his widow...'

'Oh, I see! Check whether she was reaching that point of frustration when she'd be happy to fall into bed with anyone in trousers?' Carla spat the words shakily.

'Carla, don't be stupid...' The husky voice was a touch gentler as he observed her violent anger. He leaned forward a little, his elbows on his knees, searching her taut face intently. 'You don't believe that.'

'Don't tell me what to believe! You've just...just *used* me. And it's bad enough finding out you're Leo Tremayne—the man who...who ruined my late husband's life! But what really hurts is that you already knew it, and deliberately, cold-bloodedly kept it from me, before...' she swallowed fiercely, her cheeks even hotter as she met the gleam of dry humour in his eyes '...before we had sex...!'

'That's not strictly true...'

'Isn't it? Precisely when did you remember who you were?'

'As soon as I recognised Rufus in that photograph at Tom and Becky's,' Daniel began calmly. 'But I couldn't say anything right away——'

'Don't bother concocting excuses!' she cut in. 'Even if you're telling the truth, and you remembered when you saw the photograph, you've had plenty of time to come clean! But I'm not a complete fool, Daniel. You knew ages ago, didn't you? You'd already remembered before you called on that policeman friend of yours to take you shopping! All that rubbish about having to pawn the Rolex! You deliberately deceived me. You lied to me. You've been lying to me ever since!'

There was a short, frigid silence.

'I can see what a talented detective-story writer you are,' he drawled dismissively. There was a glitter of cold anger in his eyes now. 'You've got every twist and turn neatly sewn up, haven't you?'

'What I can't understand is *why*?' She put down her tea with a shaky clatter.

'Carla...' The low, controlled note in Daniel's voice had an ominous ring. But she was too furious to pay attention.

'Unless it was simply to take advantage of the *interesting* situation you found yourself in? Make sure you got to knock off your old friend's wife, before she found out what a *louse* you were?'

'"Knock off"?' he chided sardonically. He stood up again, reached to take hold of her shoulders before she could flinch aside. He drew her up in front of him. 'What a charmingly poetic term for lovemaking...'

'Oh, *please*!' she snapped bitterly. She was shuddering with temper, under the steely grip of his hands. '*Please* don't elevate what you just did to making love...' Her stomach was knotting. That surge of response was heating her bloodstream. Her pulses were racing frantically all over again.

'OK. Reduce my side of it to animal lust. How about what you just did?' he murmured ruthlessly.

He tugged her closer, flattening her against him in one powerful, unavoidable swoop. 'You made love to me, Carla. Don't pretend you didn't. Every word you whispered, every move you made, every soft little gasp of response gave you away...'

'You really *are* a *pig*, aren't you?' she hissed back, goaded past restraint.

Bare toes were useless for kicking with. Her anger erupted, with a violent shudder. She convulsed in his grip. She tried to fight him, attack him, inflict a fraction of the pain on him that he was so coolly inflicting on her. The struggle raised the temperature. Heat flamed between them. With a muffled oath he held her prisoner, twisted her chin up, covering her mouth in a devouring, punishing kiss.

It should have made everything easier. Easier to hate him, easier to channel her anger. But the kiss confused things even more. That stubborn twist of longing sprang back to life. His lips were cool, but the heat generated burned her, right to the core. If she'd been shivering before, now she was trembling alarmingly.

'Carla, sweetheart...' The groan was wrenched from him. Sweeping her off the ground, into his arms, she found herself being carried upstairs again. This time into the small, slanting-roofed bedroom, and on to the bed. Here, catching her before she could summon the energy to spring free, Daniel pinned her easily to the softness of the duvet, and went on kissing her.

'Stop this, Daniel...' she managed to protest, beside herself with indignation and mounting desire. 'You can't just...just *ravish* me because it's easier than talking...!'

'No...?' The husky murmur held a trace of wintry humour. Mingled with a thickening layer of sexual hunger, it was a potent mix. Levering back from her slightly, he surveyed her, spread beneath him on the pale blue and grey quilt. She hadn't fastened all the buttons on the pyjama-top. The gaping fastening exposed her breasts, lifting and falling furiously as she gasped for breath. 'Just watch me, sweetheart...'

As she glared incredulously up at him, she saw his eyes darken. The slow appraisal felt as if he touched her. Like a stab of pain, her nipples tautened again. A shiver of hunger engulfed her as he added roughly, 'I'm capable of anything, remember?'

He moved possessively against her, caught both her wrists in one powerful clasp, and explored her breasts with the other hand.

'Oh, Daniel...!' Her voice broke. How could he make her feel like this again? Now? Knowing what she knew about him? Mentally she continued to rail against the onslaught. But physically, emotionally, she was lost again. There was nothing intellectual about desire, she acknowledged dimly. Or not in her case. Not with Daniel...

'Tell me what you like,' he murmured against the curve of her breasts, hunger thickening his voice. 'Show me, Carla...'

'I...*no*!' she protested forcefully, her entire body prickling with reaction as he ran hard hands down from her breasts to her thighs, moulding, caressing, exploring, tantalising. 'I can't...'

'Then I'll have to show you, won't I?' The triumphant purr caught at her senses. The arrogance took her breath away. And yet the gleam in his eyes, as he proceeded subtly to captivate her body, seemed to hold warmth, humour and desire in equal measures. This time, there was less lingering, magical build-up. Anger and passion swept through her. The small, licking flames leapt into life, like a fierce blaze out of control. The fire should have healed, but it didn't. When he stripped her again, and began to kiss every inch of her with shattering purpose, she clung and writhed and kissed him back, but the anger stayed.

With a shudder of angry despair, she dug her nails unthinkingly into his back, writhed beneath his weight with furious urgency. His lips moved across her aching nipples, and she gasped on a husky sob of pleasure. When his mouth strayed down, over the soft plane of her stomach, around the hollows of her groin, boldly invaded her most secret place, she cried out, and then she surrendered blindly, stopped fighting her senses, let the traitorous feelings flow.

'How can we be doing this...?' she breathed raggedly. She was half sobbing with need, and shame.

'The question should be...' Daniel crushed her triumphantly beneath him, lifting her hips, opening her soft secrets to him, his eyes brilliant under heavy lids '...how can we not do this?'

She closed her eyes, but twined her fingers convulsively round the back of his neck. She didn't want to see the blaze of arrogant satisfaction as he took her again, but she couldn't suppress the feverish need to touch him, to hold him. He thrust inside her with a rough groan of triumph. The power of his entry made her gasp and cry out. He began to move inside her, deep inside her, pacing his thrusts expertly, building slowly, filling her completely, and the layers of sensual pleasure mounted, one on top of the other, burying her in a dark, swirling red mist of delight.

When the build-up became unbearable, when she felt herself slipping helplessly out of control, when she contracted fiercely in climax, she dimly heard herself cry his name. There was such passionate fury in her own voice, she was taken by surprise...

'Carla...!' There was a thick hoarseness in his voice as he groaned her name. A volcanic shudder tore through him as he reached completion. It matched her own convulsive response with such savage violence, she felt almost faint with reaction...

They lay in exhausted silence afterwards. For a few seconds, his warmth was abruptly removed while he pulled the duvet over them. Then he came back, cradled her with lazy male possessiveness against him. She knew she should push him away, but somehow she couldn't. Maybe it was the aftermath of passion. Or the unearthly hour of the morning. Or the effects of the whisky she'd drunk. Or just that she didn't want to...

She turned her head into his shoulder, dazed and sated and dizzy and angry with confused emotions, and fell into the deepest sleep of her life...

The storm blew itself out overnight. Morning, when she opened bleary eyes and registered it, was full of sunshine and birdsong. More like April than November.

Senses slowly returning, she realised she was naked beneath the duvet. Slightly sore in intimate places. Stiff, as if she'd done a lengthy work-out in a gymnasium. Daniel... Turning her head quickly, she found she was alone. Where was he?

Did she *care* where he was? Details of last night filtered mercilessly back. She winced, her whole body tensing with self-disgust. Had she really behaved like that? She opened her eyes wide, then squeezed them shut again, facing the truth. It had all been so new, so overwhelming...feeling like that. Like discovering another dimension to her own capacity to feel, to experience. But no point making excuses. What a gullible push-over. Once was bad enough. Before she knew of his deception. But twice ... knowing he'd tricked her? That hinted at a severe lack of discernment ...

She climbed out of bed, retrieved the silk pyjamas, hurried into them. The navy towelling robe Daniel had worn last night was hanging on a hook by the door. She put that on, too. Belted it tightly. The cottage was silent. The clock on the landing said ten o'clock. How could she have overslept for so long?

Tiptoeing downstairs, unsure quite why she was being furtive, she found the cottage empty. Neat, clean-looking, but definitely empty.

Somewhere in the region of her solar plexus, there was a tight feeling growing. A ball of energy, confused emotion, clenching itself without warning. Had he gone for a walk? Maybe he'd gone across to the farmhouse to feed Moppy, or get some eggs for breakfast ...

An envelope was propped on the low table by the fire, supported by the copy of *The Moon's Men*. With a sudden plunge of her heart, she stood transfixed in the middle of the room, staring at it. Daniel had left a letter?

Reluctantly, she went slowly across and picked it up. His handwriting was bold, thick, looped black strokes on buff-coloured stationery. Her heart thudding, she ripped it open, and read the brief, terse note.

Carla. Sorry to duck out without saying good-bye. But getting my memory back has brought more problems than losing it. Something urgent needs my attention. I'll be in touch. Daniel.

She stared at the note for a long time, almost uncomprehendingly. Had he gone? Without saying goodbye? Back to his London office? Or to one of his offices in Europe? Or America, even?

Good riddance, she told herself fiercely. He was a hateful, mocking con man, wasn't he? She realised that she'd crumpled the note in her hand. Her anger was so intense, she could have hurled something against the wall, kicked the door. Instead, she stood rigidly, fists clenched, unsure why the fury she felt was so tangled up with pain, and an aching sense of loss...

He'd finished, got what he wanted, and gone. Well, what had she expected? Commitment? A row of affectionate kisses on the farewell note? *Endearments*? From a man so ruthless that he'd manipulated his old schoolfriend into a near nervous breakdown, and then kicked him when he was down?

Slowly, her knees buckling, she sank on to the sofa. The screwed-up letter crackled in her hand. Shakily, with numb fingers, she flung it on to the embers of the fire. The fire had gone out hours ago, but as she stared at it through tear-blurred eyes the ball of crumpled paper slowly began to move and uncurl slightly, in the residue of heat, the edges to blacken. A few minutes passed, then it finally caught fire. The flames licked high for a few seconds, then died down, until all that remained was a small pile of grey ashes.

CHAPTER SEVEN

THE following three weeks passed in a dull, painless blur. Painless, because Carla was too numb to feel. All she could do was keep her head down, and fling herself body and soul into finishing her book.

The first few days were the worst. Balancing anger and bitterness with a stubborn streak of hope. Hope that somehow she'd been wrong to judge him by Rufus's twisted standards. Wrong about his deliberate deception. His callousness...

A small part of her mind clung to this notion for as long as it sensibly could. After that, the foolish idea that Daniel would mysteriously exonerate himself, or at the very least that he would ring, write, make contact in some way, faded into thankful oblivion.

That left the numbness. And the blinkered determination to write. She resisted all attempts from Becky, Tom, and other friends in the village to draw her out about Daniel's abrupt recovery and disappearance. Instead she put all her pent-up suppressed emotion into the end of her novel, working around the clock, existing on caffeine and biscuits, until it was finished...

'Your latest book is very...powerful, Carla,' her agent murmured, over lunch in Hampstead. 'I predict a bestseller this time!'

'I thought my last one was supposed to be a best-seller?' Carla grinned faintly, picking at her prawns in saffron sauce with scant appetite. She usually enjoyed her trips up to London, the chance to dress smartly, see the capital, do some shopping. London was just about the biggest contrast she could find to her bleak, wind-swept home on the Cornish clifftop. She wasn't a city person, but she needed this injection of life and energy. In the weeks leading up to Christmas, everywhere was glittery and festive, beating the grey and icy weather which was freezing puddles and bursting pipes. The restaurant that Joe Fitzsimmons, her agent, had brought her to was warm and crowded, full of mirrors and tall leafy potplants, and expensively bohemian, resem-bling a French café.

'You know what I mean.' Joe grinned back, scanning her appearance curiously. 'This one will really keep your fans up all night. It's riveting, page-turning stuff...'

'Thanks...'

'Are you going to develop this new rapport be-tween Tresawna and Paula?'

There was a fraction of a pause.

'No.'

Joe Fitzsimmons eyed her with fresh interest. He was in his early forties, his curly hair still dark brown, a bony, ascetic-looking man with a hooked nose and intelligent brown eyes.

'My advice, as your agent, would be to develop it,' he said lightly. 'It works. There's a chemical reaction taking place between those two characters, quite independent of the intricacies of your usual plots, and the crime committed. That's the kind of thing that singles out the average detective writer from the exceptional. Don't abandon it now, Carla, or your readers will feel badly let down in the next book...'

In spite of her composure, she felt a touch of warmth creeping into her cheeks. Taking a sip of her white wine, she turned away from Joe's searching, professional scrutiny, and caught a glimpse of herself in the mirrored wall. She'd taken pains to dress up today. After the lonely, marathon haul to finish the book, in the same old denims and jumpers, she'd felt drained and plain and depressed when it was finished. Today, she wore her black velvet skirt and Victorian ankle-boots, with a soft white silk overshirt and an embroidered Indian waistcoat in glowing shades of red and purple and green. Her favourite silver ethnic jewellery completed the transformation.

Her reflection in the mirror showed it all, capped by the smooth, thick darkness of her hair, and subtle peachy shades of her make-up. But it couldn't disguise how tired and tense she felt. Her face looked pinched and thinner. Her eyes looked huge, their purplish-blue unfortunately intensified by purplish shadows beneath. 'You must eat properly, Carla,' her mother was fond of saying. 'It's no good cooking marvellous recipes once a month, and existing on toast and jam in between!'

'Is everything all right?' Joe was enquiring kindly. 'You're not eating much.'

'I'm fine. Just...tired. Burning the candle at both ends,' she said glibly.

'What are you doing for Christmas?' Joe sounded cautious. Knowing it was only a year since her husband's death, people tended to tiptoe around questions like these.

'Oh...some friends in the village have asked me to go to them...' She pulled herself together with an effort, forced a smile. 'How about you? Have you and Judith drawn the short straw again, hosting it at home?'

As their meal progressed, Joe began to talk about his family plans, and she listened with a smile fixed on her mouth, and tried to drive the bleak, painful feelings from her heart. They'd reached the coffee stage, and she was nodding and laughing as he described Judith's vow to shun cooking and buy every last morsel of festive food ready-prepared from Harrods and Marks & Spencer, when a voice beside her said, 'Carla.'

She jerked her head round in such shocked disbelief, she almost ricked her neck. She dropped the small white porcelain cup back into its saucer with a clatter which drew one or two discreet glances their way.

Daniel stood there, unsmiling. She'd almost forgotten how good he was to look at. Tall, broadshouldered, lean-hipped. In a plain dark grey suit, hard features deadpan and controlled, he looked arrogant, authoritative, every inch the successful, influential businessman. He glanced briefly at Joe before concentrating his green gaze exclusively on her again.

'Daniel.' She couldn't keep the hard edge from her voice. Compressing her lips into a cold smile, she tried to control her frantic heart-rate. 'Fancy seeing you here!'

The cliché was idiotic. And she'd only just registered that there was a woman with him. A tall, willowy, beautifully dressed blonde, with a sweetly curving mouth and wide, cornflower-blue eyes to match the woollen suit she wore. The blonde was staring at her with undisguised curiosity. Hectic colour surged into Carla's cheeks. She could see Joe's eyebrows rise a fraction. He, rather like the blonde, was watching the exchange with hawk-like fascination.

'I have to talk to you,' Daniel was saying, with cool determination. 'Am I interrupting something important?'

'Yes, you are...'

'Well, we'd just about finished,' Joe said easily at the same time. 'I'll settle up, Carla, my dear, if you want to leave with your... friend?'

'I don't...' she began stiffly, disbelieving the situation. How *dared* Daniel march up to her in a restaurant, interrupt lunch with her agent, announce that he had to talk to her? It defied belief...

The blonde had whispered something in Daniel's ear, kissed his cheek, and then disappeared out of the restaurant with a brief wave and a smile.

'Daniel Tremayne,' Daniel was introducing himself calmly. 'I'm a . . . friend of Carla's.'

'Joe Fitzsimmons,' Joe said smoothly, standing up and wryly shaking hands. 'How do you do?'

'Well, when you've both finished exchanging names and numbers,' she said icily, grabbing her handbag, 'maybe you'll excuse me? I have a train to catch. See you, Joe . . .'

She escaped on to the wet pavement outside, only to find Daniel grasping her arm and propelling her along beside him.

'You've got the most . . . monumental nerve,' she hissed, trembling with fury. 'What right do you have to haul me along like this? I'm not one of your suspects, you know! Let go of my arm or I'll scream . . .'

'Only if you promise not to run away,' Daniel countered tautly, stopping by a long black Mercedes parked at a meter in a small side-road, and pointing an electronic key to deactivate the alarm and unlock the doors. 'Do you promise?'

'Why should I promise you anything?' she shot back shakily. The shock of seeing him again, so unexpectedly, was playing havoc with her carefully prepared defences. She'd written him off as a cruel, callous monster. She'd decided she never wanted to see him again. Now, with his fingers biting insistently into her arm, his gaze locked intently with hers, she searched frantically for the ammunition to protect herself...

'Why are you so upset?' he queried softly.

'Why am I upset?' She could hardly believe she'd heard it. 'How did you think I'd feel, when you just walked out without a word? After what happened that night?'

'Relieved?' he suggested calmly. 'Your opinion of me at the time had me only just elevated from the scum of the earth. Why should you have missed me when I'd gone?'

'If you can't work that out, you're even more emotionally *deprived* than I thought!'

'Because you felt something for me?' he suggested, with ominous cool.

'Daniel, for God's sake...!' Tears had sprung, unstoppable, and began to run down her face. 'Do you enjoy torturing people? Is that the way you get your kicks?'

'If you felt something for me,' he argued, with cold logic, 'you at least owe me a hearing...' He looked tense and strained, she registered dimly. Hollow-cheeked, as if he hadn't been sleeping.

'You could have phoned me at any time in the last three weeks to talk to me,' she said stonily, dashing her hand across her face to disperse the tears. 'You expect me to believe that a...a chance meeting in a London restaurant makes you desperate to have a chat to me?'

'We can't talk standing here in the rain. Get in the car, Carla.'

'Go to hell...'

'Carla...!' With a muffled expletive, he bent and kissed her, right in the middle of the pavement, with the icy drizzle soaking them. Surprised passers-by glanced at them. But, with the rough assault of Daniel's mouth on hers, Carla felt a convulsive shudder right through her body. She shut her eyes, forgot for the moment to fight, instead drank in the waves of bittersweet sensation. How many nights had she lain awake, thinking about Daniel kissing her?

He released her, and she staggered slightly. He steered her into the passenger seat, and clunked the door decisively closed. When he came around and got in beside her, she couldn't bring herself to look at him.

'Where am I being *abducted* to?' she demanded unsteadily.

'Don't be melodramatic, Carla,' he said, with a bleak smile. The smile lifted her spirits slightly, despite her anger. It reminded her of one of the things about him she found so irresistible. His sense of humour...

Her thoughts stopped short, and she froze, appalled at herself. She didn't find *anything* irresistible about Daniel Tremayne! This was a man she knew to be a ruthless manipulator. A tyrant. A liar...

They were driving through heavy traffic, turning into an exclusive square with tall white Regency houses. There were private gardens, fenced in with black railings. A pram was being wheeled out of the gate, hood and rain-apron snugly fastened, in the charge of what looked to be a uniformed nanny. Did Daniel live here? In this millionaire-priced part of London?

'My flat's on the top floor,' he said briefly, ushering her out of the car and in through a security-locked entrance, 'but there's a lift. You look malnourished. Haven't you been eating?'

'I'm perfectly all right, thank you.'

'If you say so.'

The top floor was thickly carpeted in navy blue, with cream and gold paper on the walls. Daniel's front door opened to reveal plenty of space, a wonderful city view of roofs, chimneys, and leafless gardens, and the warm glow of antique pine furniture. The place had an odd sense of welcome. Carla found herself walking slowly into the sitting-room, and lowering herself warily on to a soft crimson sofa, apprehension flooding through her.

'It's not the rural peace of Cornwall,' Daniel said ruefully, slipping her coat from her shoulders, 'but it's not bad for a city base. I've been thinking of buying a country place to escape to at weekends. Can I get you something to drink? Coffee? Tea?'

'Nothing, thanks.'

'I'll make some tea.' He grinned at her white face, and disappeared into the kitchen. 'Strong and sweet...?'

The taunt seemed to stir her back to life. Jumping up, she marched into the kitchen.

'Don't you dare!' she said with as much firmness as she could manage. 'I am *not* in shock. You really are the most conceited man I've met!'

'Hey, slow down on the compliments.' His glance was bleakly amused. 'I'll make coffee, then. You liked my coffee, remember?'

There was a silence. She watched him move around the room, economically and efficiently. He'd loosened the green silk tie, unbuttoned his top shirt-button. A suggestion of five o'clock shadow shaded the lower part of his jaw. Abruptly, she swung away. It hurt to watch him. If only she'd resisted his persuasion, outside the restaurant...if only she *had* screamed, attracted unwelcome attention, anything to spare her this painful confrontation in Daniel's London flat...

'I'm sorry I haven't been in touch,' he said flatly, carrying a tray of coffee back into the sitting-room, and flicking on a gas-log fire. 'God, I hate these things. The flames are there but they don't burn anything...'

'Yes...' She took her cup, and sipped it, tensely. Daniel might be a ruthless pig, but he made a good cup of coffee, she could say that for him. And she felt exactly the same way about real fires...

Daniel met her eyes, and held her gaze for a few seconds.

'Carla, I know what you must have thought. When I walked out and didn't contact you. But...'

'Daniel...' She stopped him, suddenly overcome by anger and indignation. Did he honestly think, having bumped into her again on the off-chance, he could spin her a line? Put everything right? Pride, long overdue, came to the rescue. Straightening up, clamping her tumultuous feelings firmly back in place, she met his gaze unblinkingly. 'Don't insult me with some trumped-up list of excuses. Please?'

He stared at her, his mouth suddenly grimmer.

'Trumped-up excuses?' he echoed softly. 'Is that what you think you'll hear?'

She managed a cool little smile.

'It's what I know I'll hear,' she tossed back at him. 'And the truth is, Daniel, there's no need to go to the trouble. What...what happened that night in the cottage was just one of those things...'

'Just one of those things.' Daniel said it reflectively. There was an ominous lack of expression in his voice.

'Will you please stop repeating the end of my sentences?' she continued neutrally, avoiding his eyes. There was a pain in her stomach. A dull ache. It wouldn't go away. She took a deep breath, and tried to concentrate on her train of thought,

'It was something that just...just overtook us. Let's face it, we hardly *know* each other. We still don't. It didn't mean anything.'

'So you're saying it's all over, you're not interested in getting to know each other better?'

She shrugged stiffly. 'Why should we bother? OK, sex...' She cleared her throat. Her voice was getting annoyingly husky. 'Sex between us was good. But that's no basis for anything. Especially as I didn't know a thing about you...for all I know, you could be married.'

'I'm not.' Daniel spoke with a trace of steel in his voice. 'I'm thirty years old, single, healthy and heterosexual. And are you in the habit of *meaningless* casual sex with total strangers?'

She glared at him resentfully. 'Look, I offered you the cottage. I told you why. But, even if you hadn't turned out to be Leo Tremayne, there'd have been no future in it. I'm...I'm not in the market for another relationship...'

'Are you involved with someone else? You looked pretty friendly with the man you were lunching with.' The wry bleakness in Daniel's tone made her glance at him quickly.

'With Joe...?' Her brain whirled rapidly. Did he suspect her of an alliance of some kind with *Joe*? Slowly, she linked her hands together in her lap, and lowered her eyelids. She had to do this, she flayed herself silently. She had to extricate herself from this mess with minimum damage... 'How...how did you guess?' she said in a low voice.

'Are you saying you are involved with him?' His voice hardened.

'Did you imagine I lived the life of a nun?' she countered huskily. Inside, she was dying, twisting in anguish. 'Anyway, you looked *very* friendly with the blonde girl who was with you.'

Daniel leaned slowly back in his seat. He didn't take his eyes off her white face. But abruptly he raked his fingers through his thick dark hair. His mouth twisted cynically.

'You mean Rachel? Oh, I am. *Very* friendly. Rachel and I have known each other all our lives. In fact, it was Rachel's cottage I was borrowing, just along the coast from Penuthna.'

'So... that's where you were staying? Before the accident?' She felt her heart contracting.

'Yes. I'd left my car in her garage, taken the coastal path. I'd planned to call and see you, then have a pub snack in the village and phone for a taxi back. But then the cliff gave way and...' he grinned bleakly '... you know the rest.'

'That's nice...' she heard herself saying wretchedly.

'Nice?' Daniel's gaze was quizzical.

'I mean, nice to... to have a relationship with someone you've known a long time. It's easier to know where you stand with someone, if you've known them for ages...' She was hardly making sense, she knew. The revelation about Rachel seemed to have robbed her of sensible speech... Rachel. The owner of the initial 'R' on Daniel's mystery note? Definitely, she deduced, with bleak satisfaction. 'Daniel, darling...' She felt something clench inside her, and fought down waves of misery.

She bit her lip at the gleam she detected in Daniel's narrowed gaze.

'Did you know where you stood with Rufus?' he probed, softly ruthless.

Carla stared at him. The switch of topic had taken her by surprise, but given her a safety-line...

'I...yes. I knew where I stood.'

'Did you? Did you, Carla?'

She could feel her hands beginning to tremble, and she clasped them together more tightly.

'Daniel, what are you getting at?'

'Did you know that one of Rufus's motives for marrying you was because your parents had plenty of money?'

The heat flooded her, and then drained away so swiftly, she felt icy cold. Wide-eyed, she somehow managed to keep her gaze fixed on Daniel's.

'Oh, yes,' she whispered bitterly. 'I knew. At the time I didn't, but very soon afterwards. Deep down, I told myself I was lucky. Who else would have wanted me?'

'What the *hell* are you talking about?' He sounded hoarsely incredulous.

'Rufus obviously filled you in on all the sordid details,' she said shakily, 'so I expect he told you I was a...a plump, spotty *swot*, and that my father couldn't wait to palm me off on whoever made the best offer?'

The silence following this declaration was so prolonged, she thought Daniel was lost for words. Finally, he said with a slow grin, 'So what happened to the plump, spotty swot? When did the ugly duckling turn into a swan?'

'I wasn't angling for compliments,' she snapped tautly, loathing him for his teasing. 'Just filling you in on the details you might not have been familiar with...'

'Is that really why you married Rufus? Because you thought no one else would want to marry you?' The humour had died from his eyes. He sounded incredulous.

'No... I'd had a crush on Rufus for years...'

'Tell me what happened, Carla.'

There was something in Daniel's tone, some subtle quality, that prompted her to pour out the past. With quiet bitterness, she said, 'Rufus was quite... glamorous. Dark red hair, piercing blue eyes. His family, the Ryans, had inherited wealth but they'd lost nearly all their money. They'd enough in trust to complete Rufus's education, but then, unlike his contemporaries, he had to make it on his own in the world. You'd know all that anyway. My father knew the family through farming connections. I think I told you that, didn't I? Dad was chairman of an international farm machinery company. They were family friends. So I saw Rufus a lot when I was young. Sort of hero-worshipped him...'

'You hero-worshipped *Rufus*?' The tease was gentle. She met his intent gaze, and couldn't resist smiling a fraction.

'Yes. I did. When he went away to school each term, I pined terribly. I convinced myself I would love him forever...'

'And did you? Did you love him, Carla?'

'I thought I did, at first,' she admitted shakily. 'But quite soon after our marriage I realised I'd made a mistake. He...he'd changed so much. After hating Sandhurst, and then after his fiasco with your company, he didn't really seem to know what he wanted. He came back to Cornwall bitter and twisted. I just didn't realise until it was too late...'

'He didn't change, Carla. You just got to know him better.'

She stared at him then. 'You really hated Rufus, didn't you?'

Daniel shook his head slowly. 'No. I didn't hate him. Hate is too great a waste of energy for bastards like Rufus——'

'He was my husband,' she cut in, in a strangled voice. 'He's been dead only a year! How can you sit there and say that?'

'I'm not intending to be callous. I didn't want to deliberately hurt you, Carla...'

'You just can't help it!'

'I'm being honest. Realistic. We both knew Rufus. Like it or not, he's played a major role in both our lives...'

'As the victim, in your case!'

'Not true. Rufus came into the business full of his own importance, after dropping out of Sandhurst...'

'And you were jealous!'

'No, I was not jealous,' Daniel said calmly, watching her white face, 'I was ambitious. I had plans to make the business succeed. What I couldn't cope with was Rufus treating it like a part-time cash-cow. Rufus was the reason the company started to go downhill—strolling in when he felt inclined, sleeping off hangovers when he didn't, dipping his hand into the petty-cash tin to go gambling with his spoilt, rich friends who were playing at jobs until they inherited Daddy's wealth, and never bothering to pay it back, screwing up important jobs because he either wimped out, or forgot to turn up at the crucial time. I didn't defraud Rufus of a penny. I bought him out, fair and square, when he'd squandered all his money on his wasted lifestyle. I continued to employ him because we were old friends. But when he tried to move in on my sister, and break up her marriage, enough was enough...'

Until now the calm annihilation had made painful listening. The last part made Carla stiffen incredulously.

'Never speak ill of the dead,' she lashed softly. 'Poor Rufus isn't around to refute any of this. How convenient for you! And, as for your sister's marriage, it takes two to tango, isn't that the phrase they use ... ?'

'My sister was in a low state,' Daniel said, soft steel in his voice. 'Her husband was abroad. She'd just had a miscarriage. She was depressed. Rufus started making a play for her, by pretending to cheer her up with flowers and chocolates and trips to the theatre. He borrowed God knows how much money from her, on the pretext of forgetting his chequebook, or losing his credit card. It wasn't until he made a heavy pass, got rejection, then lost his temper, that I found out about it ...'

Carla went very still. A heavy, twisted feeling had descended, somewhere in the region of her heart. She didn't want to listen. She didn't want to hear.

'Carla ...' Daniel probed quietly. 'Did he do that with you? Lose his temper? Over sex?'

She couldn't say anything. She couldn't move. Finally she managed a brief, stiff nod, and shrugged.

'Yes ...'

'Carla, sweetheart ...' He reached to take her hand, holding it tightly in both of his.

'Don't, Daniel, please ...'

'Carla, believe me, I'm not proud of demolishing Rufus's reputation. He's dead. He can't answer back. I know that. But I had to defend myself. You threw some damning accusations at me, that night in the cottage. I'm not a martyr. I can't pretend they're true, just to salvage your husband's image...'

'It's all right,' she said coldly, pulling her hand away with supreme control. 'Rufus and I were married for three years. I won't pretend it was a happy marriage. There's not much image to salvage. It doesn't matter, Daniel. It's all in the past...'

'It matters to me,' he countered, 'and I think it matters to you. I'm setting the record straight. I'm not the ruthless villain of your fantasies...'

'OK. Point taken. Is that all?'

'Carla, for the love of heaven...'

'Is that all you wanted to talk to me so urgently about? Just to set your personal record straight? Can I go now? I've got a train to catch...'

'Oh, God, this is useless...' Daniel caught her hand again, and pulled her, rigid and unresponsive, into his arms. Holding her there with one taut arm, he tilted her stiff face up, searching her eyes with a shadowed, bleak stare.

'To hell with Joe Fitz-whatsisname,' he grated angrily. 'You can't be serious about him—can you?'

'Of course I can,' she retorted, catching her breath as Daniel stroked his thumbs possessively along her jawline, caressed them up towards her temples. 'Joe and I have had a . . . a relationship for years. In fact he's probably the most important man in my life...'

'Kiss me,' he ordered softly, his eyes on her parted lips. 'Kiss me, and then tell me you'd rather be with Joe.'

'No...!'

'Do you *want* to go now,' he switched tack softly, 'or do you want to stay here, with me, and do this...?' He dropped his head to kiss her, covering her parted lips with cool, deliberate expertise. His controlled assault threatened to annihilate her shaky defences...

'Daniel...'

'I want to make love to you, *now*!'

The throaty command against her lips made her tremble. Words seemed to have deserted her. With a strangled sob, she felt the familiar, ominous heat of surrender beginning to consume her, inch by inch, melting her, weakening her. He caressed the line of her neck with sure, confident fingers. He lingered on the frantic throb of her pulse in the hollow of her throat, then moulded arrogantly lower. He slipped his hands inside her waistcoat and cupped the jut of her breasts through the silk of her blouse.

'You still feel something, Carla. I know you do...'

There was a dangerous gleam in the dark green eyes. It matched the husky, hypnotic sensuality of his voice. She was shaking all over...

'Don't you...?' He tugged open the buttons of her blouse with cool determination. His gaze raked the exposed jut of her breasts, narrowing on the tell-tale tightness of her nipples where they thrust traitorously through the cream satin of her bra...

'No...' she repeated, on a strangled sob.

'No?' His voice was thicker. A slight shudder went through him as he moved his head down to trail a moist, warm, tantalising string of kisses across her heated skin, his mouth open and sensuous. Shuddering with helpless need, her stomach contracted in violent response. She let her fingers clench once, convulsively, in the thick darkness of his hair. Then she tensed and pushed him fiercely, as hard as she could.

'Stop it!' she breathed raggedly, gasping at the effort to defend herself. 'There's no point, Daniel, I told you; I'm involved with... with Joe! I'm not interested...'

Slowly, Daniel released her. He was breathing unsteadily. His eyes darkened on her white, set face. She tried to decipher his expression. There was a gleam of desire, but another quality in his gaze which unnerved her even more...

'I don't believe you.' The clipped, suppressed emotion in his voice caught her by surprise, but it was too late...

'Because you're too thick-skinned and arrogant!' she hurled back passionately, crossing her hands protectively across her breasts. 'And besides, what about *Rachel*?' she added on a choked sob. 'I'm sure you'd rather be with her! Isn't that why you took off that morning, leaving nothing but a curt note, and didn't bother to ring or write afterwards? How can you put on this…act, Daniel, expect me to believe you're sincere? We bump into each other by chance, in London, and now you're pressuring me to renege on a close relationship with Joe? Just for the sake of another quick session in bed with you, maybe? *Forget* it!'

'Carla, *listen* to me…' The husky command tore at her composure.

'No!' Her voice cracked, rose a fraction as she pushed herself away from him, pushed herself free, snatching her open blouse together with hands that shook uncontrollably.

'Just leave me alone, Daniel. Do you hear me? Leave me alone! I don't *want* you in my life! I never want to see you again! *Never*!'

CHAPTER EIGHT

'HAVEN'T you thought about locking your door at night?'

Carla, startled out of her wits, dropped the holly-wreath she was twisting together with garden wire, and swivelled round. Daniel stood there, lounging calmly at her kitchen door, while a blast of cold wind and rain swirled in around him.

She opened her mouth to speak, but no sound came out. Daniel, here in Cornwall? Finally, graciously, paying her the long-awaited visit? It was a week since their fraught confrontation in London. Three days till Christmas. She'd convinced herself she'd never see him again. In fact, she'd even convinced herself she didn't want to. That she'd meant every word of her last, fierce declaration, meant it right from the bottom of her heart . . .

'I'm surprised you're not more security-conscious, with an imagination for writing detective novels,' he was adding coolly, strolling inside and pushing the door closed behind him. 'I could have been some desperate pervert, seeking a victim.'

'Your words, not mine,' she managed at last. Somehow she kept her voice controlled. 'What *are* you doing here, Daniel, apart from seeking a victim?'

149

'We're neighbours again, temporarily.' He eyed
the pile of pine-twigs, fircones, dried flowers and
shiny Victorian baubles with a gleam of bleak
humour. 'Rachel and I were spending a few days
at her cottage. She wanted some help to get it ready
for the Christmas break. I thought I'd drop by and
say hello.'

'You needn't have bothered.' The quiet bitterness in her voice was impossible to hide. Rachel's
cottage? He was down here again with Rachel? A
vision of the blonde girl swam into her mind. Wavy,
shoulder-length hair, soft blue eyes, a figure to die
for...she felt almost physically sick thinking about
Daniel sharing a cottage with the girl. 'I told you
I never wanted to see you again. I meant it.'

'So you did.' Daniel's tone was hard to judge.
Was he deliberately goading? Calmly accepting?
Mockingly taunting?

She couldn't tear her gaze away from him. His
thick black hair looked tousled and damp. In dark
green twill trousers and a charcoal cashmere
jumper, the gleam of a white silk shirt visible at the
neck, tan leather flying-jacket, he was so over-
whelmingly male, so ruggedly attractive, he brought
an unwelcome prickle of heat to her skin.

'Then why are you here?'

'I don't like loose ends.' The glint in the green
eyes made her heart miss a beat, in spite of the icy
feeling inside. 'I think we should talk. Don't you?'

'What about?'

'About what happened a few weeks ago.' He slanted a harder look at her, adding quietly, 'I owe you an explanation, Carla. Even if you don't want to hear it.'

'You're right. I don't want to hear it. So I'm not being given any choice, is that it?'

'That's it.' There was a gleam of his usual humour behind his cautious smile. 'So go and get changed. I'm taking you out for dinner.'

'Won't *Rachel* mind?'

'No. She won't mind.'

'How convenient!'

'Rachel loves me deeply, but she's not the jealous type.'

'And if *I* don't want to go out for dinner?' She felt cold inside. Shivery with anger, and misery. What a cool, cynical bastard he was!

'I'm sure you can suffer one last night of my company.'

His words sank in. Staring at him, she felt her stomach tighten. One last night? The dark, despairing feeling was back. What was wrong with her? She wanted this over, finished, didn't she? So why this agonised pain inside?

Her head spinning, she considered the options. She could throw him out, refuse to listen, although, knowing Daniel's thick-skinned arrogance, he'd undoubtedly refuse to be thrown... She could break down and beg him to leave, but that would only show her vulnerability. Or she could put on the most

impressive performance of her life, and pretend she
was indifferent...

Glancing at her watch, she shrugged slightly.

'I suppose I could spare a couple hours.
I'm...I'm expecting an important phone call
later...'

'From *Joe*?' The mocking cynicism set her teeth
on edge.

'Yes. From Joe...'

'OK.' Daniel's voice had hardened. 'I'll have you
back here for your important phone call, Carla.
We can't have Joe kept waiting, can we?'

'Daniel, I...'

'Go and get changed,' he advised peremptorily.

With a mutinous look, she was about to argue,
but the ominous glitter in his eyes sent her hurrying
out of the kitchen, and almost running up to her
room. It was at times like this, she thought furiously, plunging beneath the shower and then haphazardly scanning the contents of the wardrobe,
that she could do with not only remembering to
lock her outer doors, she could do with a guard
dog, and a lock on her bedroom door too...

The restaurant he drove them to was an ancient
Cornish inn. It had polished flagstones and what
looked to be half a tree burning in the huge ingle-
nook fireplace. From the rows of expensive cars
outside, and the lack of prices on the menu, it was
clearly in the high-price bracket.

'Carla...' Daniel was eyeing her with an air of
wary amusement over the flicker of candlelight.

'Would you please try to relax enough to choose what you want to eat?'

She blinked. Her fingers were holding the heavy red leather menu so tightly, her knuckles were white. She couldn't pretend to be relaxed, she realised forlornly. Even wearing the ego-boost of her new Monsoon suit, in the softest of plum-coloured silks, with her silver moon earrings and Celtic cross, she felt so tightly wound up, she might explode at any moment.

'You choose,' she suggested flatly. 'I'm not very hungry.'

'Right.' With a lift of his hand, he conjured the head waiter out of thin air. 'We'll have the lobster bisque, the chicken breasts in brandy and cream. Sauté potatoes. French beans. And a bottle of Sauvignon.'

The waiter collected their menus with a deferential murmur, then dematerialised. Daniel eyed her levelly across the table.

'I never got around to buying you dinner,' he said calmly. 'In fact, I never got round to thanking you properly...'

'Thanking me?' A cold feeling was closing over her heart. The tone of this evening was so...final. Furious with herself, she discarded the notion. She loathed him. She *wanted* it to be final...

'For saving my life.'

'Don't exaggerate. You know perfectly well I did no such thing! Anyway, if that's what tonight is all about, I don't want your...gratitude.' She spoke as evenly as she could, her eyes cool. 'I wouldn't have expected it at the time. It means even less now as a rather half-hearted afterthought. Forget it, Daniel.'

'That's hard to do,' he mused implacably. 'We may only have been together a short time, Carla, but we got to know each other fairly... intimately. Wouldn't you say?'

She glared at him, willing herself not to blush.

'Only superficially, I'd say,' she countered abruptly. 'Most of the time I didn't even know who you were! Neither did you!'

Daniel grinned. 'Technicalities. It was more... a meeting of souls, I felt.'

The cool, slightly teasing note in his voice was more than she could stand. How could he be so cruel? Gripping her hands together, she forced herself to say quietly, 'I learned that you have a black sense of humour, and no conscience at all, if that's what you mean.'

'I think you do our brief romance an injustice,' he argued mildly. 'By the time you fell into my arms and demonstrated such a deliciously amorous nature, sweetheart, we'd discovered all sorts of things in common, hadn't we?'

'Such as?'

'Cornish cliffs in the moonlight?' he taunted softly. 'A penchant for detective work? A serious allergy to Rufus Ryan?'

'Daniel...!' Her choked warning died away, and she dropped her eyes.

'Yes, Carla?'

'If I'm going to sit here and eat this ... this last dinner with you, can we please talk about something ... uncontroversial?'

The light in his eyes was unreadable. He shrugged slightly.

'Did you finish your book on time?'

'Yes. I burnt the midnight oil a bit. My publishers are very pleased with the story.'

'Good. So now you're free to relax for a while? What are you doing for Christmas?'

'I'm going to Becky and Tom's.' She was hanging on to her temper with growing difficulty. This was a charade, she realised bitterly. Daniel Tremayne being his usual crass, insensitive, cynical self. He didn't care how much he'd hurt her, just leaving the way he had, without an explanation, never bothering to ring or write ...

The night they'd spent together had been earth-shattering for her, meant very little to him. If he ever found out how deeply she'd been affected by their lovemaking, she'd die of shame. Daniel was a typical 'action' man. He'd have no way of understanding how a magical transformation had taken place inside her that night. How the years of doubt and insecurity had vanished. How Daniel's kiss, his touch had combined to create a melting warmth and desire she'd never known before ...

So much for that strange sensation that they were destined to meet, meant to be together. That was melodramatic rubbish. That feeling she'd had when she'd sat in the moonlight, gazing at his unconscious figure halfway down the cliff. The strong impression of having known him before, in some mythical previous existence...total insanity. She must have been under mental pressure with her deadline... Yet something still eluded her. Niggled at the back of her brain, persistently, disturbingly...

The ache inside her was growing. Bleakly, she realised he was saying something to her. She jolted back with difficulty.

'Sorry...?'

'I said, what's your mother doing?' he repeated softly, watching her warring emotions with deadpan concentration. 'For Christmas?'

'She...she's going on a Caribbean cruise. With her bridge friends. I drove up to Bath yesterday and we exchanged presents...'

'You're not close to your mother.' It was a statement more than a question. Slowly, she shook her head.

'That's an understatement,' she agreed, with a degree of bitter irony.

'That's a pity.' Daniel sounded thoughtful. 'My parents are both dead. I miss them much more around Christmas time. Especially when I come back down here. They came from North Cornwall. Near Port Isaac. If there'd been bad feeling between us, it would be a lot worse.'

Carla let out a shaky sigh.

'I know. I've been trying to heal the rift. My mother and I get on superficially. I mean, we talk on the phone regularly, I worry about her health, she worries about my diet and safety, makes all the affectionate noises, says all the things mothers are supposed to do...but the truth is, she and Dad wanted a son. I was never exactly the apple of her eye...'

'Are you serious? You think your mother still holds it against you for being the wrong sex?' Daniel sounded incredulous.

'Totally,' she assured him bleakly. 'And when Rufus died in his riding accident, and I blurted out to her the truth about my marriage, about his...his drinking, and his violent fits, she was horrified. She took his side. Stood up for Rufus, and accused me of lying. Virtually said I hadn't tried to be a good wife to him...'

She stopped, abruptly. How did Daniel manage to do this, every time? Get her to pour her heart out, even while she mistrusted him, resented him?

'Go on...?'

'That's it,' she finished flatly. 'That's definitely enough soul-baring on my side. What about you?'

'Me?' His tone was enigmatic.

'Yes. What are *you* doing for Christmas?'

'I've had a few invitations. I'm not sure yet. Right now, I'm more interested in you. Carla, sweetheart...'

'Don't call me your sweetheart,' she snapped, goaded past caring about her façade of calm.

'It's time you accepted yourself as you are.' Daniel had leaned back in his chair, observing her intently, ignoring her outburst. 'Stopped wondering if you disappointed your parents, disappointed that unspeakable bastard Rufus. Time you stopped seeing yourself as that unattractive teenager you described to me in London. The duckling turned into a swan a long time ago, Carla. Deep down you've got to start believing that. It's time to have more faith in yourself. Be proud to be a beautiful, desirable female. Forget Rufus, and his twisted personality. Forget your parents' curious attitudes. Those were their emotional problems, not yours——'

'You've got the nerve to sit there and ... and *pontificate* about my self-image,' she cut in, almost quivering with fury, 'when you treated me like *dirt*?'

'Carla...' His voice had deepened, hardened, but she shook her head furiously.

'Don't deny it! It's not that I care,' she added bitterly, dimly conscious that this tirade threatened to expose her feelings in all their pathetic intensity, 'but if you think your...deceit, your pretence, your cynical taking advantage of me was guaranteed to boost my self-image you're a lousy amateur psychologist, Daniel! I'm sick of men, sick of their *hypocrisy* ... !'

Daniel had gone paler. He flicked her an unreadable glance across the table.

'I'm going to tell you a story, Carla. I want you to listen. Then decide whether it should have a happy or a sad ending. Agreed?'

She stared at him mutinously, then shrugged. She forced herself to stay detached. Otherwise she'd burst into tears...

'Agreed?' he repeated, his voice cooler.

'All right.' She evaded his eyes, staring at the huge log on the fire. She'd get nowhere gazing at the firm shape of his jaw, staring at his beautiful mouth and recalling how it felt on hers...

'There was a man who lost his memory. He met a girl, and immediately he fell...' The firm mouth twisted as she shot a bleak glance at him, but his eyes remained expressionless. 'He felt attracted to her. He wanted her. He wanted to make love to her. So much, he couldn't sleep at night...'

'Daniel, for heaven's sake...!' The husky voice and the compelling quality of his gaze was bringing colour to her cheeks.

'You agreed to listen.'

'Yes.'

'Then he remembered who he was. And the coincidence was that he was right where he set out to be. Visiting the widow of an old schoolfriend and ex-business partner. And when she knew who he was the girl hated him, because of what she thought he'd done to her late husband. Are you with me so far?'

'It sounds rather similar to something that happened to me recently.' Carla managed a bitter half-smile, in spite of her anguish.

'The next day, when he woke up, he remembered even more. He phoned his offices in London, and heard they'd been trying to contact him. There was a crisis he had to resolve. One of his key employees had been kidnapped by a criminal counterfeit circle operating in Hong Kong. There'd been an ultimatum...'

'Daniel, this is beginning to sound like a bad remake of a James Bond film...'

'You said you'd listen.'

The wine arrived, was tasted, approved, and poured. She sipped some, and felt the fortifying effect with gratitude.

'The ultimatum was that unless a large ransom was paid the key employee would have his throat cut——'

'Oh, good grief...!'

'Will you stop interrupting?'

'Sorry.'

'The man decided that the criminal counterfeit circle would cut his employee's throat whether they got the money or not. So he caught the next flight to Hong Kong and set about trying to find the key employee. This took a fair time. However...' Daniel levelled a lidded, wry gaze at her '... before he left for Hong Kong, he tried to telephone the girl, to tell her he wouldn't be in touch for a couple of weeks. But there was never any reply from her telephone...'

'But...'

'The man remembered, then, a similar fault on the telephone in the cottage he'd rented from the girl. Was it possible, he wondered, that telephone

engineers were working on correcting the lines, and
making the girl uncontactable? Just at this crucial
point in his story?

'Events then overtook the man, leaving him no
more time to arrange his social life. His mission to
Hong Kong went wrong. He tracked down the
criminal counterfeit gang, then discovered that, instead of being in mortal danger, his key employee
was in fact alive, free, and operating a double-bluff
to get the ransom money for himself...'

'Oh, Daniel...!' Shocked into total attention,
she gazed at him. 'That's dreadful...'

'The man briefly contemplated cutting the key
employee's throat himself to vent his frustration,
but luckily his genteel upbringing came to the
rescue.' Daniel's wry glance was bleakly comical.
'But when he finally sorted out the mess, dispensed
with the services of the key employee and exposed
the counterfeit gang to his clients, he resurfaced in
London feeling slightly shell-shocked. He decided
that after all this time a telephone call to the girl
would seem insulting. He resolved to drive down
there and see her, and try to sort out the problem.
Meanwhile, he had lunch at a restaurant in London,
and there, by another strange coincidence, who
should he see but the girl from Cornwall, laughing
and lunching with another man. You probably
know the story from that point on...'

There was a long, fraught silence. Carla found
she was hardly breathing. The arrival of their soup
provided a small distraction. Finally, she said

quietly, 'Daniel...when...when we met in London, why didn't you just tell me about Hong Kong? About the crisis?'

'You didn't give me a chance. All you were interested in was throwing insults and accusations at me.'

'Because I...I was hurt,' she admitted slowly. 'Your...your involvement with Rachel was half expected, I suppose. I mean, you were bound to have had a...a satisfactory personal life, before you lost your memory. I wasn't naïve enough to imagine you'd lived like a monk until you fell off the cliff...but you'd remembered, before we spent that night together. Remembered Rachel, who you were, who you were involved with... You deliberately deceived me, Daniel. But I thought you'd have at least rung, even to say forget it, nice knowing you...'

The soup was no doubt delicious. But she could hardly taste it. She lowered her spoon, and faced him despairingly.

'But when you found out I was Rufus's old enemy you didn't want to know me,' he reminded her, with a ruthless grin.

She was silent, in turmoil.

'Is it true? About the phone being out of order?' she said at last.

'Would I lie to you?'

'Possibly.' She shrugged, and gave a short laugh. 'Definitely. You already have. About getting your memory back...'

'I admit to an ulterior motive that evening.'

'Which was?'

'Playing for time.' Daniel shot her an ambiguous smile, and tackled his soup with apparent relish. After a few minutes, he sat back and regarded her coolly across the table, an ominous gleam in his eyes.

'As things had turned out, the playing for time was unnecessary, wasn't it? You were committed to another man all along. Which means that far from being the innocent victim in all this, Carla, you've been far from totally honest with me...'

'That's not quite the way I'd put it...'

'It's the way I see it.'

'So...' She shrugged, colour creeping into her face. Her heart was pounding so hard, the blood was drumming in her ears. She felt ill with nervous tension. 'Where does that leave us?'

'Quits, I'd say.' Daniel leaned back, his eyes hardening. 'With the slate wiped clean?'

She felt as if she'd been neatly backed into a corner. Was this the triumphal way Daniel dispensed with all his unwanted romantic liaisons? she wondered feverishly.

'Yes,' she heard herself say, with commendable lack of emotion, 'I suppose it does.'

Their main courses arrived. She forced herself to take control. Calmly, feeling numb inside, she helped herself to vegetables, accepted more wine, took a mouthful of the chicken. It was exquisitely cooked. The sauce was mouthwatering.

She glanced across at Daniel. He appeared to be quite relaxed, enjoying his meal.

'So... what's Rachel doing tonight?'

The question drew a slant of mockery, and Carla cursed herself. No amount of self-control could have stopped her asking.

'Rachel's driving back up to London. She and her husband are spending Christmas there.'

In stunned silence, she gazed at him.

'She and her husband?' she repeated finally, laying down her knife and fork. 'She's married?'

'Yes.' The gleam in Daniel's green eyes was unbearably taunting. 'Yes. Rachel is married. Happily married, as a matter of fact...'

'But her relationship with you...?'

'Her relationship with me is an extra in her life... something totally different.'

Sick at heart, she stared at him.

'I see. She likes... variety?' The bleak disgust in her voice communicated itself to Daniel. His gaze hardened a fraction.

'Why so disapproving?' he countered mildly. 'Isn't this rather a case of the pot and the kettle?'

She felt the colour blanch from her face.

'What?'

'For someone involved in an extra-marital affair herself, to be passing judgement on others?'

'What on earth are you talking about...?' The words died on her lips. Her heart plunged painfully. Joe. Of course, Joe Fitzsimmons. She might have guessed that someone like Daniel would have checked him out ... What had she got herself into, with one little white lie?

'You did some private detective work, I gather?' she fenced lightly. 'I suppose that's the kind of behaviour I should expect from a private detective?'

'Naturally. I must say, I was disappointed in you. I hadn't classed you the type for adultery.'

She coloured involuntarily. Her temper soared.

'That's a nerve, coming from *you*!'

'Mmm. Maybe we should accept each other as flawed personalities?' Daniel suggested blandly. 'What intrigues me, though, is the notion that you could be a touch ... jealous?'

'Oh, for goodness' sake,' she snapped softly, her colour deepening. 'Just because we had ... a brief fling together? Why should I be jealous about an existing relationship?'

'Search me.' The green gaze was bleakly amused. 'Unless ...' there was a trace of cool arrogance in his voice '... your feelings for me go deeper than you're prepared to admit?'

'You're so damn conceited ... !'

She felt her eyes lock with his. There was a magnetism in his gaze which threatened to scatter her fragile defences. She dragged herself together with an inward shudder. Pride might be one of the deadly sins, but in this case it was the only shield she had. The mere thought of blurting out her fantasies, laying them out before Daniel to watch them trodden into the ground, sent shivers of panic through her.

'Am I?' He grinned, his eyes lidded as he assessed her reaction. 'Oh, I almost forgot. Rachel asked me if you'd mind signing your latest book for her? I've got it in my coat pocket...'

Carla blanched. She could hardly believe her ears. Was Daniel really so totally devoid of normal sensitivity? He might not have guessed the depth of her feelings for him. He might believe her to be involved with Joe Fitzsimmons. But surely even Daniel couldn't have mistaken her naïvely abandoned lovemaking that night for complete disinterest?

Daniel had gone across to the coat-stand by the door of the restaurant, to delve into the deep pocket of his flying-jacket. He returned to their table, with a copy of *The Lion's Share*, and handed it to her expressionlessly.

Carla stared blindly at the cover. It had been published in the summer, a faintly allegorical story. A glossy-looking golden lion adorned the cover, lying regally beside a subtle suggestion of a body, hidden in a pile of leaves. She took it, her fingers shaking.

'Me, sign a book for Rachel?' she echoed stupidly. 'Is this some kind of... of joke?'

Suddenly, his closeness just across the table from her seemed intolerable. It made her want to turn and run.

'It's no joke. Rachel's a fan of yours. She's anxious for your autograph on your latest book. She was very excited to see you in that restaurant in London. She'd always thought Carl Julyan was a man. And a much older man, so she told me. Is there some reason why you shouldn't sign it for her?'

'What would you like me to put?' she whispered coldly, a harsh catch in her voice. 'All my love, Carla?'

'That would be nice.' He sounded thoughtful. 'Though I'd rather you addressed that to me...'

She stared at him, anger pulsing through her in waves, her throat drying. Why had she tried to fool herself she was immune to him? This man could hurt her more with a single sentence than Rufus had been able to with three years of mental and, occasionally, physical cruelty...

Jerkily, she pushed her chair back and stood up.

'I'd like to go home now, please,' she said, in a strangled voice. 'Will you take me? Or shall I call a taxi?'

'Rushing back for Joe's phone call? Sure, I'll take you.' Daniel stood up too, an odd quality in his voice, a harder gleam in his eyes. Dimly, as her coat was fetched, the bill paid, the short, rain-soaked walk to the car completed, she sensed a subtle aura of triumph about him. The feeling disturbed and infuriated her, almost as much as his sledge-hammer tact had devastated her...

'So you won't sign Rachel's book?' he persisted, as they turned into the dark country lane and began the drive home.

'*No!*' She couldn't help it. Pain and bitterness engulfed her. Staring blindly out of the windscreen, her eyes on the swish of the wipers, she felt rather than saw his brief glance across at her.

'Pity.' Something in the nonchalant taunt of his voice made her turn to stare at him suspiciously. 'I promised Rachel that Carla Julyan and I were like *that*——' he held up two fingers twisted together, with a shadow of a grin '—and I hate to disappoint my favourite sister.'

CHAPTER NINE

THE silence seethed with tension.

'Your *sister*?' Carla finally managed the two words. She felt hot, then cold. She was shivering with pent-up anger and indignation.

'Yes. Rachel. My sister.' Daniel's deep voice was bland, as they wound their way through the narrow lanes, back to Penuthna. 'Sorry. Didn't I say before that she was my sister?'

She let out her breath on a shuddering, explosive sound.

'You know damn well you didn't,' she said in a low voice. 'You've deliberately led me to believe she was your...your *girlfriend*!'

She hardly knew how she felt, tense as a coiled spring in the passenger seat. All she knew was that she hated Daniel, with his cruel sense of humour, his cavalier attitude to her feelings...hated him so much she felt like kicking and punching and screaming, and venting all her bitter anger on him...

'You jumped to that conclusion,' he was musing mildly. He pulled into the courtyard of the farmhouse, and cut the lights. A brilliant moon shone in through the windscreen. The rain had stopped. The panorama of the cliffs, the sea and the distant

spires and turrets of St Michael's Mount lay ahead
of them, silvered and drained of colour.

'And you didn't correct me,' she pointed out
stiffly. She wished she could unravel her feelings.
Humiliated, embarrassed, resentful, indig-
nant...or simmeringly, volcanically furious...

'You were so intent on thinking the worst of me,'
Daniel murmured, turning to inspect her with an
unreadable light in his eyes. There it was again, she
realised, that aura of triumph about him. It was
the last straw. With whiplash fury, she snapped
open the car door and got out, strode to the front
door. Hearing Daniel behind her, she swung round
abruptly.

'Don't think you're coming in,' she grated
huskily. 'Go away. Go away, leave me alone, and
don't come back...'

Impervious, he walked in ahead of her, switching
on the lights, inciting her to such anger, she was
trembling all over.

'If I'd studied martial arts, I'd probably kill you
right now,' she hissed, watching him bend to light
the fire laid in the hearth in the sitting-room.

'Unlikely. How do you think I defend myself
against criminal counterfeit gangs et cetera?'
Teasing humour glinted in his eyes.

'They wouldn't have the same motivations I've
got...'

'Carla, will you just cool down a bit?' he suggested, his grin like a red rag to a bull. With a gasp
of pure rage, she flew at him, fists flailing.

'How *could* you trick me like that?' she stormed, uncaring where the blows fell. 'How could you, Daniel? Knowing how I'd feel? After that night together...?'

She made contact with his jaw, and his chest, before he managed to deflect the frenzied assault and immobilise her.

'Now we get to the interesting part,' he murmured hoarsely, tightening his arms round her when she squirmed to escape. 'How *did* you feel, Carla?'

'If you think I'm going to humiliate myself for your entertainment...'

'Humiliate yourself? Why should feelings be humiliating?' He spoke with soft roughness, and when he prised her head back to search her face she saw that the humour was bleak, the amusement tinged with wary intensity...

'I'm not about to make a complete fool of myself over any man again...' she began in a shaky whisper. 'But you knew how I felt, when we made love...'

'Mind-reading being my speciality?' he queried wryly. The steel band of his grip eased a fraction.

'You didn't need to be a mind-reader!'

There was a taut silence. Abruptly, Daniel swung her around and sat her down on the sofa in front of the fire. Coming down beside her, he took hold of her shoulders. She turned her head away and he gave her a slight shake, forcing her to look at him.

'Let's get a few things straight,' he said evenly. 'I wanted to take you to bed the minute I saw you. I spent most of the time here suppressing the urge.

Like I said at the time, it wasn't a good idea. First, because I didn't know what or who I was. Second, because when I did know I knew you wouldn't like it! I remembered when I saw the picture of Rufus. No earlier, despite your accusations. I exerted maximum control that night. I went to bed in that cottage, burning up with frustration, alone. Then the police woke us both up, you appeared at my door in wet satin pyjamas and...that was that. God, Carla, I'm no saint...'

'Tell me something I don't know,' she murmured bleakly. But her pulses were drumming, the blood was surging through her veins so fiercely, she could almost hear it...

'So sex was great.' There was a harder edge to his voice. 'But sex is sometimes a side issue...'

'In your life, maybe...'

'Hear me out,' he warned, his voice roughening. 'It's a side issue when it's not the only thing holding two people together. For you, I felt the strongest desire I've ever felt for any woman. But I felt a lot more than physical desire for you, Carla. I got the impression it could have been mutual...'

'So you decided to walk out on me, then torment me by making me so jealous I couldn't sleep at night?' she retorted in a choked voice.

'Carla...' The green gaze was wryly intent on her face, his voice huskily ironic. 'You were shattered when I told you my name. Suddenly you found you'd just made love with your husband's greatest enemy. The way you looked at me wasn't the way you look at someone you care for, and respect...'

'No.' There was a lump in her throat. It wouldn't go. She didn't want to burst into tears. That would be pathetic. Rigid with effort, she controlled herself.

'I had to leave fast. My note was honest. I didn't want to go, but I had to. Even without the Hong Kong problem, I'd probably have run out on you that morning. There was too much to think about. Too much to get straight in my mind. Getting my memory back. The bizarre coincidence, finding I was with Red's wife. I didn't know how the hell you felt about me. In the back of my mind, I thought you probably hated me—for Rufus, for deceiving you, for dragging you up to my bed, like...like a...'

'Like a lion with its prey?' she suggested, with the faintest gleam of a smile.

'Yeah...that'll do.' The answering glint of humour in Daniel's eyes made her heart squeeze with anguished regret.

There was a disturbing tingle of reaction in her shoulders where Daniel's hands held her. Through the soft plum silk, the warmth of his touch seemed to burn.

'For all I know, you still hate me for Rufus.'

'I...no. No, I don't hate you for Rufus.' Her voice cracked, on a throat so dry, she suddenly craved water. Twisting herself shakily free, she stood up. Her knees felt like alien joints, not belonging to her body. Slowly she made it to the kitchen, filled a glass with water, drank it quickly.

Daniel had followed her to the doorway. When she turned, he was watching her. The dark, rugged lines of his face were so mesmerising, she literally had to wrench her eyes away.

'Did you want some?' She gestured to the glass.

'I think I need something stronger.'

'There's wine in the fridge. Or brandy... in the sideboard in the sitting-room.'

'Brandy, I think. Join me?' The wry gaze seemed to see right through her. Shakily, she shrugged and nodded.

'So has Rufus's ghost finally been laid to rest, Carla?' He led her back to the sitting-room. The fire was catching well. Flames were licking round the coal, tonguing up over the log balanced on top. The room smelled of pine. The white candle lights on the Christmas tree in the alcove by the window were warming the branches. The resiny smell was so unique to the season, Carla felt her throat tighten again. She took a gulp of brandy, and drew a deep breath.

'Rufus's ghost has never haunted me,' she countered quietly. 'I can't pretend feelings for him I never had. And you may have deceived me over a few things, but on the subject of Rufus I... I do believe you.'

'That's a start.'

'It... it wasn't until you came along that Rufus's past made any sense to me. I'd seen it through his eyes only. Your version made sense. Knowing him as I did, it made sense...'

'Carla, sweetheart . . .' She stiffened. Fear was uncurling inside her, so sharp and potent, it made her feel cold, frozen inside.

'Daniel, please don't . . .'

'Don't what? Say "Carla, sweetheart"?' he murmured, his eyes narrowed. 'Why does that upset you so much, I wonder?'

The gleam in his eyes was hypnotic. She felt so lost in his gaze, she hardly knew what she was saying. 'Because it makes it sound as if you . . . as if you *cared* for me. Makes it sound like that to me, that is. It makes me *think* you might care for me . . .'

She was barely coherent, she realised, squeezing her eyes shut and willing herself to stay detached.

'And that upsets you?'

'Yes . . .'

Without warning, he reached an arm along the back of the sofa, and touched her cheek lightly, with one long finger. His touch felt like a mini electric shock.

'Why? Why should that upset you?'

'Because . . . I might forget to be careful,' she whispered huskily. 'I might . . . let myself believe all sorts of fantasies were possible . . .'

'Fantasies?' Daniel's voice held that dry amusement, underlaid with an emotion she didn't recognise. 'You have fantasies about me?'

'A few.'

'Tell me about them . . .'

'*No!*' Her vehemence made him laugh. Leaning a fraction closer, he slid his fingers around the nape of her neck, and stroked the delicate hollow there. The caress sent tremors, feathery reactions of pure pleasure and delight, trickling right down to her thighs, her toes...

'Tell me, Carla,' he probed, softly ruthless. 'I need to hear.'

'Just... fantasies.' Her throat felt choked, her cheeks hot. 'Silly, dream-like feelings... feelings that we were meant to be together... like that night I found you, on the cliff, in the moonlight...'

'Ah, moonlight.' Daniel didn't move any closer. His voice sounded lightly husky, as if he was suppressing his emotions with cool restraint. 'My mother used to tell a story about the moon. It was where all the wasted treasures of the earth were stored...'

'Wasted treasures?' She turned to look at him. The choked feeling in her throat was worse. It was spreading to her chest. To her solar plexus. Making her heart feel as if it was expanding uncomfortably against her ribcage...'

'Broken vows, misspent time and wealth, unanswered prayers, fruitless tears...'

'That's a beautiful story,' she agreed in a muffled voice, twisting her head away.

'There are dozens of beautiful myths about the moon,' he went on calmly. 'Maybe it's because it's so important to us. We measure time by it. Time is the most precious thing of all. The treasure that we waste the most...'

'Daniel...' Slowly, she turned her head and met his eyes again, her stomach clenched in knots of uncertainty. 'Daniel, I...'

The telephone rang. The sound of the shrilling bell shattered the intensity of the moment. For a few seconds she sat there, frozen to the sofa.

Daniel glanced at his watch, with apparent coolness.

'Half-past ten. Was this when you were expecting a call from Joe?' The non-committal, unemotional way he spoke seemed to shred her nerves.

The truth hit her with a sick jolt. He *didn't* care. Not the way she did... If he cared, he'd surely be jealous about the idea of her having an affair with Joe? Daniel, as he'd said, just didn't like loose ends. He'd just come to straighten things out, clear the air between them. One last night of his company, he'd said. She'd conveniently forgotten that warning, almost bared her soul under his charismatic influence...

How could she have been so gullible? The painful realisation felt like a small death in her heart.

Jumping stiffly to her feet, she went to pick up the phone. Joe's voice spoke at the other end of the line. Composing herself, fortified by the brandy on top of the white wine over dinner, she adopted her most seductive voice.

'Joe! How *lovely* to hear from you...'

There was a pause.

'Er...thanks. You sound surprised... I did say I'd ring tonight about that deal, didn't I? Are you all right, Carla?'

'I'm fine. Never better. How are you?'

'Fighting off the flu, since you ask. But well enough to let you know your Christmas present. I've clinched that American deal for your last four books...'

'*Wonderful*...' She injected all the husky emotion she could summon into her voice. 'That's just...*wonderful*! Joe...I have to see you soon...'

'Well, not before Christmas. But yes, of course. An idea for another book?' He sounded perplexed, but hopeful.

'Mmm...definitely...' she purred, conscious of Daniel's presence behind her. 'You won't be able to resist it——'

She was abruptly cut off as Daniel snatched the receiver.

'Joe?' he said tersely. 'Daniel Tremayne. Carla has to go now. She'll be in touch. Happy Christmas, love to Judith and the kids. *Ciao*...'

The receiver was dropped back in its cradle. Daniel swung round, the expression in his eyes so mercilessly intent, she involuntarily took a step back.

'Daniel, how dare you cut in on my telephone call?'

'Forget the act, Carla...'

'And how long have you been on first-name terms with Joe, and Judith? "Love to the *kids*"...?' She was breathless with fury.

'I said cut the act...' Too fast for her to evade him, he snaked out a hand and grabbed her arm, pulling her to him. 'Just what the *hell* do you think you're playing at?'

'Daniel...' He looked so angry, she quaked inwardly, but her own anger gave her the courage to fight. 'I don't care if you see yourself as the original macho-man; nothing gives you the right to treat me like this...'

With a rough expletive, he stopped her incensed protest with his mouth. Her bubble of fury silenced, he moved in ruthlessly. She shuddered in helpless indignation as he held her still. The contact burned, ignited such fiery passion, she could almost feel the flames licking around her. His mouth withdrew, for a breathless moment, then covered her lips devouringly again. His tongue forced entry, plunged deep in her mouth with a hunger that sent her stomach into spasms of need.

'Carla, I know the game you've been playing,' Daniel groaned, levering himself a few inches apart from her, his eyes narrowed on her flushed face, 'but I need to hear the truth from you...you're not involved with Joe Fitzsimmons. Are you?'

It was more of a hoarse, arrogant statement than a question. Warmth crept into her face. But embarrassment was swamped by the new heat, a different heat...

When she didn't reply, he tightened one hand furiously around her neck, moulding her cruelly closer. With the other, he captured her chin, tilting her face up for merciless inspection.

'Are you, Carla?' he demanded tersely.

'Why would it matter to you?' she whispered unsteadily.

'Do I have to show you?' There was a furnace of angry desire erupting between them. The flare of heat was like a pain, ripping through her. Helplessly, she arched herself instinctively against him, wanting the intimate feel of him moulded with her body, hungry with need for him, caution deserting her...

Raking a possessive hand along her back, he lifted his other hand to the sensitive line of her jaw, stroking her face with his thumbs, his fingers thrusting into the thickness of her hair above her ears...

'Do I, Carla?' he reiterated. There was a light in his eyes, brilliant enough to dazzle her. But there was darkness there too. A depth of darkness she couldn't understand. She shivered despairingly.

'Only if you really mean it.' It was a half-sob, so quiet, she hardly heard it herself. Daniel's narrowed gaze had grown fiercer. With a thickened groan, he picked her up and strode to the sofa, depositing her and coming down to pin her there, his fingers dispensing with the buttons on the purple silk jacket with rough impatience.

'I really mean it,' he muttered unsteadily. 'Sweetheart, I mean it...'

The silk was soft, and slithered beneath his hands. Shyness and reticence gone, she twisted feverishly, helping to free herself of the impediment of clothes, Daniel's impatience transmitting itself to her. By the time she was naked, the last wisp of lace removed, she was trembling so violently, Daniel's mouth quirked in wry self-mockery.

'You're shaking. Am I still so terrifying, Carla?'

'Yes...' It was a husky whisper, but she reached up quickly and pulled him against her, half laughing, half crying, the storm of emotion overwhelming her totally. 'But please don't stop... please, Daniel...'

'Hey...' His eyes held that ironic gleam she found so irresistible. 'Just give me a second to dump these clothes, sweetheart, and I'm all yours...'

She gave a small choke of laughter, through the tears.

'All mine?'

'Every last inch, Carla...' The smile he gave her held wicked humour, and a deeper intensity which made her heart pause, mid-beat, then jerk jubilantly to life again. Wildly, no longer caring if this bewildering passion was reciprocated, she let her fingers stroke and explore, heard her own voice moaning softly as Daniel's caresses and kisses became bolder and more demanding. As he plundered her mouth, her breasts, the soft quiver of her stomach, the moist velvet intimacy between her thighs, she abandoned any hope of pretence. Pride could be resurrected later, she told herself in the far, far recesses of her brain, where logical thought was still possible. Need, her need of Daniel, was the only thing that mattered right now...

She cried out, though, when he took her with a rough hunger which brought her vulnerability painfully back to the surface.

With a thick groan, he kissed her, long and deep, framing her face with slightly unsteady hands as, with a shudder of barely restrained violence, he thrust fully inside, completed the full male invasion. 'Sorry, sweetheart...' His mouth was against her lips, his powerful hardness gloriously welcome as he pinned her to the sofa. His breathing was ragged, his voice hoarse. 'Are you OK? Am I hurting you?'

'No...no...' The whisper was torn from her. He hadn't hurt her, not physically...she was alight with shimmering, tantalising, ecstatic arousal...it was the inequality of things that frightened her. He had so much strength, power, hunger. It was evident sexually, but it mirrored their differences in other things... An awareness of her own female limitations, her vulnerability, sent shivers along her nerve-endings...

'Daniel...oh, Daniel...' But the soft voice was hers, paradoxically warm with invitation and desire and feminine longing.

'Sweet little Carla,' he muttered, 'I've wanted you so badly...oh, God, darling, yes...yes...!'

His powerful, forceful movements combined with his husky words were intensely exciting. The furnace flared white-hot, without warning, the shudders of completion rocking her from her head to her toes, with after-shocks that seemed to go on and on, like tremors after an earthquake. With a choked sob, she clung to him, and blindly let the flames consume her...

'I thought when I came clean about Rachel you'd do the same about Joe.' It was much later. Daniel's eyes were warm and possessive on her flushed face and starry eyes. 'So why the hell do I still have to drag it out of you?'

'Well...' She wriggled in the warmth of his arms. They'd subsided to the floor, in front of the fire. The only lights in the room were the white candles on the Christmas tree, glowing on red and gold baubles and green tinsel, and the flicker of fire-light. Daniel had suggested they go upstairs, but Carla didn't want to move. She didn't want to break the spell... From being a bleak prospect, her heart in pieces, Christmas had abruptly become a mir-aculous, glowing time, full of love and endless, joyous possibilities...

'Why did you trick me for so long about Rachel?' she asked softly.

'To reassure myself. If you got jealous, I knew you cared.'

'Same thing goes for me,' she said with a choked laugh. 'You can't blame me for doing the same thing.'

'So do we have this straight now? Rachel is my sister. Joe Fitzsimmons is your *agent*,' he reminded her with soft mockery, 'just your agent. Your happily married, family-man literary agent?'

'Yes.'

'Carla...'

'Yes, *yes*!'

'And you're not having an affair with him!'

'No. I fully confess. I made it up. In self-defence. Satisfied?'

The green eyes searched her face ruthlessly.

'Almost.'

'How did you get so...friendly with him?' she demanded huskily as he tightened his arms round her. They'd pulled on most of their clothes again eventually, rather haphazardly. Even with the log fire burning it was going colder. It rarely snowed in Cornwall. But there'd been rumours that there might even be a white Christmas... 'Did you go and see him?'

'You bet.' Daniel's hard face was at its most devastating, calmly sardonic, but with such a brilliance in his eyes, she felt her breath catch in her throat. 'I was made decidedly welcome. Had tea, met the family. The works.' His mouth twisted with humour. 'Joe appeared to have been curious as hell about your last book—he'd suspected some new mystery man in your life, responsible for heating up the relationship between your Inspector Tresawna and his quiet little sidekick Paula...'

'*What*?' Carla found herself speechless.

'Yup. And when he met me he was *naturally* keen to get to know me better, so...'

'I do not believe this,' Carla said slowly, laughter and anger spiralling uncontrollably. Anger temporarily won. 'I do *not* believe I'm hearing this! Of all the...the chauvinistic, patronising...oh!'

She stopped abruptly, her eyes widening as she gazed at Daniel.

The truth dawned. In a great blinding flash, the truth dawned. The reason Daniel had seemed so familiar all along... the reason she'd sensed a link, a powerful connection...

'Carla?' His quirked eyebrow was teasing.

'Oh, no...' she breathed shakily. 'Oh, heavens, I've just realised... it's just come to me...'

Daniel's quizzical look became ominously patient.

'Are you going to expand on this mysterious revelation, Carla?' he growled softly. 'Or do I have to torture it out of you?'

'I...' She bit her lip. The sudden knowledge was so momentous, she'd gone very still and quiet inside. 'You say Joe thinks *you're* responsible for "heating up" my Inspector Jack Tresawna?' she whispered at last, with a slight, embarrassed laugh. 'Well, as a matter of fact...'

Daniel's patience was showing dangerous signs of cracking. He was projecting that wry, motionless concentration she knew spelled trouble.

'*Yes*?'

'He's you,' she finished up, slightly breathless and decidedly incoherent. 'I mean... you *are* Jack Tresawna... or rather Jack Tresawna is *you*...!'

There was a stunned silence.

'Could you run that by me again?' he drawled at last.

'I've only just realised. Unconsciously, I based my hero on you. I know we hadn't met... but Rufus used to get drunk and treat me to endless bitter stories of Leo Tremayne's legendary exploits. I started creating my ideal man in Jack Tresawna. But I didn't recognise the source of my inspiration. Until now. Just this very minute...' She risked a glance at his expression. 'Oh, lord, I should have kept this to myself,' she finished up, her cheeks becoming warmer under that hawkish, predatory grin. 'I knew it! Your ego was inflated enough already...!'

'Don't worry. I won't crow for long. Give me a couple of years and I'll be as modest and self-effacing as ever.'

'You will?' She met the laughter in his eyes and her heart seemed to swell.

'I will. And now we know how to keep Joe and your readers happy—they just want more of the same in your next masterpiece,' he grinned unrepentantly.

'Hmm...'

His gaze darkened on the softness in her eyes. 'And to tell you the truth, Carla, I want more of the same, right now...!'

It was a teasing groan against her hair. With easy strength, he hauled her closer. The heat from his body flooded her, defusing her slight tension.

'And you want it too,' he taunted huskily.

'Maybe...' she whispered, suddenly hot with shyness, even after their recent lovemaking, overwhelmed with the depth of her own emotions. 'But Daniel, I'm frightened...'

'*Still* frightened? Of me?' The soft query was abrupt. Picking her up in his arms, he carried her back to the sofa, sat down with her in his lap, his hands roaming hungrily over the feather-soft silk of her suit. 'What can I do to reassure you? I'm a single white male, certified disease-free. I admit to a number of Jack the Lad relationships. But I was free when I met you. I have a healthy bank account. I don't have a police record. I can supply references for good character...'

'Don't you ever stop joking?' she blazed at him, half angry, half laughing with mounting, secret joy.

'Don't be frightened of me, Carla,' he advised, the laughter fading. She found herself caught up in his gaze again, and this time neither of them smiled.

'I...I'm frightened of myself. Of the way you make me feel,' she explained huskily. 'I've never felt this way before, about anyone. I...I've had this silly fantasy that we were somehow meant to be together. Predestined...! I couldn't bear the pain if I let myself love you, then lost you...'

'I like your fantasies, sweetheart,' he teased tenderly. 'I've had a couple like that myself. About you. And why should you lose me?' His voice was rougher. 'What I had in mind was a fairly permanent arrangement.'

'Fairly permanent?'

'Permanent. Until the advent of the Grim Reaper, which will hopefully be postponed at least a hundred years...'

Her heart seemed to stop for a second. When it started again, its beating was so frantic, she thought it must crack a rib.

'Are you saying... ?'

'I don't know what I'm saying.' He grinned raggedly. 'I'm no good at this. But I know what I mean. I love you, Carla. I want to marry you. I've never asked a woman to marry me before. Marriage is a state I've avoided while I devoted my time to playing cops and robbers. But I'd had time to think about this. It's not a spur-of-the-moment decision. It's what I want. So for God's sake, sweetheart, don't turn me down. I love you. I love you, Carla...'

Shining-eyed, she gazed at him. Disbelievingly. Purple-blue eyes locked intensely with sea-green.

'Are you real?' she whispered ruefully, quelling the idiotic urge to burst into tears of happiness. 'You're *not* a... a psychic disturbance of my imagination, are you?'

'No. I'm real...' His mouth twitching, Daniel slid his hands along her shoulders, and slowly, tenderly traced the smooth line of her throat. She shut her eyes. A shiver of pure delight brought goosebumps to the surface of her skin.

'Are you sure? You're not Jack Tresawna, come to life?' she demanded unsteadily, receiving a derisive grin in return. 'Are you sure I didn't invent you, that night on the cliff, in the moonlight... ?'

'I'm sure. And another thing is for sure,' he said decisively, kissing her hard on her parted lips, 'the moon won't be getting any unanswered prayers for its mythical treasure-haul, sweetheart. You're everything I could ever pray for...'

Their eyes met, and they smiled at each other. The depth of feeling conveyed was more than words could ever express.

'Can we go upstairs?' he suggested hoarsely. The message in his narrowed gaze was sending her temperature soaring to fever point again.

Without waiting, he scooped her up in his arms, and carried her towards the bedroom. Carla hooked her arms round his neck, gazing up at him with loving, laughing eyes.

'Still, meeting my inspiration in the flesh, as it were...has caused a problem,' she murmured solemnly, though her eyes were dancing like stars. 'I'm wondering how I'm going to overcome it...'

'Carla, sweetheart, do you love me...?'

'Mmm...yes, I think I love you!'

'You only think?'

'I know I love you!' she laughed breathlessly, wincing as his arms tightened like steel bands.

'That's better. If you love me——' Daniel's wry smile flipped her heart right over '—there's no problem we can't overcome.'

'But there might be. The thing is...' she grinned as he laid her firmly and victoriously on the bed and trapped her there '...do you think anyone would notice if in my next detective story Inspector Jack Tresawna's eyes mysteriously changed from blue to green...?'

Barbara

DELINSKY

A COLLECTION

New York Times bestselling author Barbara Delinsky has created three wonderful love stories featuring the charming and irrepressible matchmaker, Victoria Lesser. Worldwide are proud to bring back these delightful romances – together for the first time, they are published in one beautiful volume this September.

THE REAL THING
TWELVE ACROSS
A SINGLE ROSE

Available from September   **Priced £4.99**

W RLDWIDE

Available from WH Smith, John Menzies, Volume One, Forbuoys, Martins, Woolworths, Tesco, Asda, Safeway and other paperback stockists.

NORA ROBERTS

◆

SWEET REVENGE

Adrianne's glittering lifestyle was the perfect foil for her extraordinary talents — no one knew her as *The Shadow*, the most notorious jewel thief of the decade. She had a secret ambition to carry out the ultimate heist — one that would even an old and bitter score. But she would need all her stealth and cunning to pull it off, with Philip Chamberlain, Interpol's toughest and smartest cop, hot on her trail. His only mistake was to fall under Adrianne's seductive spell.

AVAILABLE NOW   **PRICE £4.99**

W☻RLDWIDE

Available from WH Smith, John Menzies, Volume One, Forbuoys, Martins, Woolworths, Tesco, Asda, Safeway and other paperback stockists.

Next Month's Romances

Each month you can choose from a wide variety of romance with Mills & Boon. Below are the new titles to look out for next month, why not ask either Mills & Boon Reader Service or your Newsagent to reserve you a copy of the titles you want to buy – just tick the titles you would like and either post to Reader Service or take it to any Newsagent and ask them to order your books.

Please save me the following titles:	Please tick	✓
A MASTERFUL MAN	Lindsay Armstrong	
WAITING GAME	Diana Hamilton	
DARK FATE	Charlotte Lamb	
DEAREST MARY JANE	Betty Neels	
WEB OF DARKNESS	Helen Brooks	
DARK APOLLO	Sara Craven	
BLUE FIRE	Sarah Holland	
MASTER OF EL CORAZON	Sandra Marton	
A WAYWARD LOVE	Emma Richmond	
TANGLED DESTINIES	Sara Wood	
THE RIGHT KIND OF MAN	Jessica Hart	
DANGEROUS ENTANGLEMENT	Susanne McCarthy	
THE HEAT OF THE MOMENT	Kay Gregory	
AN EASY MAN TO LOVE	Lee Stafford	
THE BEST-MADE PLANS	Leigh Michaels	
NEW LEASE ON LOVE	Shannon Waverly	

If you would like to order these books in addition to your regular subscription from Mills & Boon Reader Service please send £1.90 per title to: Mills & Boon Reader Service, Freepost, P.O. Box 236, Croydon, Surrey, CR9 9EL, quote your Subscriber No:................................... (if applicable) and complete the name and address details below. Alternatively, these books are available from many local Newsagents including W H Smith, J Menzies, Martins and other paperback stockists from 14 October 1994.

Name:..

Address:..

....Post Code:..........................

To Retailer: If you would like to stock M&B books please contact your regular book/magazine wholesaler for details.

You may be mailed with offers from other reputable companies as a result of this application. If you would rather not take advantage of these opportunities please tick box. ☐